Speaking Human

A Journey in Palliative Medicine

Craig C. Durie

First Edition

Table of Contents

Dedication

This book is dedicated to my mother and father, Elizabeth and Barry Durie, who at the earliest points in my life equipped me with many of the foundational skills required to do this work. In a broader sense, this book is also dedicated to all of us engaged in the work of caring for others, whether as a clinician, family member, or friend.

Disclaimer

This book includes stories of a medical nature. Personal health privacy is important to me and a protected component in practice. All of the names in these stories have been changed to honor that privacy. In addition, location, dates, age, ethnicity and gender are altered to further protect individuals and families. Any resemblance to personal events can only be associated with the generalizable nature intended in these stories.

I am a nurse practitioner with twenty-five years of experience in healthcare, a decade of which has been in palliative medicine. The Center to Advance Palliative Care defines this discipline as:

> specialized medical care for people living with a serious illness. This type of care is focused on providing relief from the symptoms and stress of the illness. The goal is to improve quality of life for both the patient and the family. Palliative care is provided by a specially-trained team of doctors, nurses and other specialists who work together with a patient's other doctors to provide an extra layer of support. Palliative care is based on the needs of the patient, not on the patient's prognosis. It is appropriate at any age and at any stage in a serious illness, and it can be provided along with curative treatment.[1]

Palliative care is often confused with hospice, but there is a distinct difference between these two areas of practice. In the United States, hospice is a Medicare benefit that focuses on end-of-life care when disease modifying treatment is not available or desired and life expectancy is an estimated six months or less. While palliative care can occur toward the end of life, it's main focus is providing comfort and seeking clarity during a time of serious illness. It can be paired with treatment and the inclusion of palliative care during a hospital stay does not mean the patient is dying.

---

[1] "Palliative Care Definition: What Is Palliative Care," Center to Advance Palliative Care, last modified September 7, 2016, https://www.capc.org/about/palliative-care/

Ernie—the Beginning of COVID-19

My first COVID case was not a COVID case. In January of 2020, the United States saw its first case of the novel coronavirus that came to be known as COVID-19.[2] It took time for a national consciousness to develop surrounding the growing threat. The medical community began awakening and preparing faster than the community outside of the hospital, though our level of preventative measures also grew in fits and starts. In the hospital where I practice, masks were mandated relatively early. Visitation cautions began to fall into place in late February and March of 2020. By then, my household was thankful to have a delivery service for food and, of all things, an adequate supply of toilet paper.

The impact on our lives varied and largely depended on our level of vulnerability, education, and personal thoughts on risk mitigation. At one point, we were Lysol-spraying mail and groceries after letting them sit, untouched, for days. In early March, Governor Wolf announced that all schools in Pennsylvania would close on March 16 for a minimum of ten days.[3] Those ten days expanded to include the

---

[2] AJMC Staff, "A Timeline of COVID-19 Developments in 2020," AJMC, last modified January 1, 2021, https://www.ajmc.com/view/a-timeline-of-covid19-developments-in-2020

[3] CBS21 News, "Governor Wolf Announces Closure of All Pennsylvania Schools," WHP, last modified March 13, 2020, https://local21news.com/news/local/central-pa-schools-announce-major-changes-due-to-covid-19

remainder of my daughters' school year. I began wearing scrubs to work and changing in my garage before going through a decontamination routine as I entered my home. Then it was a Clorox wipe to the pager, phone, phone case, and ID badge, not to mention the meticulous washing of the hands. I wasn't really home until my tied plastic bag with the day's scrubs was upstairs.

It was in that atmosphere of uncertainty and anxiety when I provided my first COVID-19 consult to a patient in one of our intensive care units (ICU). Ernie arrived at our hospital from an assisted living community with COVID-like symptoms consisting of fever and mounting dyspnea. In mid-March, all Lehigh Valley regional hospitals had jointly announced visitor limitations. That effectively meant no visitors in the ICU and later evolved to only permit visitation for the actively dying. The whole world of palliative consultation and family meetings was about to change.

The consult request for Ernie read simply, "goals of care." Ernie had gone far past being short of breath since his admission and was engaged like a machine in the task of breathing. He was wearing a BiPAP mask compressed to his face with supplemental oxygen at 85 percent. Some of his goals had already been clarified—he had documented "no CPR and no intubation," meaning no insertion of a breathing tube. A review of the chart also told me he had advanced COPD, heart disease, and diabetes. It was not his first admission that year.

At nine o'clock in the morning, there were rarely visitors. Still, it was odd to check in with his nurse and realize there wouldn't be any during the course of Ernie's hospital stay. Family visitation influences a patient's well-being, and a family's advocacy can also guide relevant decision-making. With a BiPAP mask in place, it also effectively meant that Ernie would not be able to hear a phone call over the noise, nor did he have the air to shout back to a caller. His isolation room became more than just four walls and a negative pressure airflow. He was truly cut off from his family who lived less than ten miles away.

The emergency department (ED) had administered Ernie's COVID-19 test three days before. Unfortunately, at that stage of the pandemic, results of testing sometimes took ten days to return. I would be checking in with Ernie to see if his thought on declining a ventilator held while also seeing what I could offer in symptom management. Given how difficult it was for him to breathe and his poor oxygenation, any conversation had to be right to the point.

The steps to get to Ernie were not as straightforward as sliding the glass door open and walking in. He lay in a negative pressure room, which was dutifully taking the room air through a filter and venting it outside the hospital. I would be entering through an anteroom after taking off my lab coat and donning a yellow isolation one, gloves, an N95 mask, cover mask, and goggles. I squeezed the nosepiece, and if my goggles didn't fog, I knew the seal was good. Then, I stepped into a room potentially full of aerosolized COVID particles to engage in a conversation that sometimes lasted in excess of thirty minutes. In all that gear, I don't think I could appear more remote from humanity if I tried.

Ernie tracked me as I entered and barely took the time to hear me introduce myself or the role of palliative medicine. He didn't have the air nor the patience for dialogue. It turned out I wouldn't be the one who would have to tactfully decide how to be both empathetic and direct.

He pulled his lips back together against the pressure of forced air within the mask and began to form words above the volume of the apparatus. "I…want…you…to help me die."

I pulled up a stool to be eye level with him. Wisps of gray hair puffed in the burst of air escaping from the top of his mask.

"Okay," I said in a tone meant to convey I wasn't there to tell him what to do. "If we take the mask off, you'll probably die. We can also give you medications to keep you comfortable."

Ernie said, "Okay…Let me go." I quickly affirmed the documented code status and negotiated for some time to contact his family. He agreed to let me call his daughter before we made any adjustments to his treatment plan. We were in a brief holding pattern.

The conversation had been shorter than I was comfortable with, given the gravity of Ernie's demands. I processed what he'd said as I went through the minutes-long routine of shedding all of my gear to exit his room. He had been forthright and lucid. His message was consistent with what he had expressed to nursing and what had triggered the consultation.

Ernie was seventy-eight, and his wife was deceased. His next of kin was his only daughter, Clarice. After alcohol-gelling my hands for the umpteenth time and putting a fresh mask on, I picked up the phone to call her. I sat with Ernie in my line of sight from the alcove desk adjacent to his room. Clarice answered on the first ring. I introduced myself and went on to explain the purpose of this palliative medicine consultation.

"My name is Craig. I'm a nurse practitioner and part of the palliative medicine service here at the hospital. My team was consulted by the critical care team, and my role is to work with patients and families dealing with complex healthcare challenges, navigate decision-making, and manage symptoms."

Her answers began to help me understand where to begin the conversation.

"I heard he was having a hard time breathing and that it's worse than it had been over the last two months," Clarice said. "I know his heart isn't in great shape, and his lungs are probably even worse. He's been needing oxygen on and off most of the year, and he doesn't seem to recover much. I know he's in the ICU, which can't be good."

"You're right. He is in the ICU, and he's working pretty hard to get air. In fact, we're trying to help him with that by using a pressurized mask called a BiPAP. It works a little bit like an external ventilator to push concentrated oxygen in. It's a bit uncomfortable and makes it hard to talk. We're also giving him some steroids to open up his lungs as well as some diuretics to help move some fluid. His chest x-ray looks abnormal, and we're giving him some antibiotics while we wait for his COVID test results to come back. This may be a combination of his lung disease and heart disease with pneumonia on top of that."

It felt like it was too early in the conversation to share with Clarice what her father had told me. I needed to know more about Ernie the person and less about Ernie the patient. So, I asked her to fill in the gaps for me.

"Tell me more about your father. What did he do for a living, and what did he do for fun? Given his health struggles over the past year, what still puts a smile on his face?"

I could hear the color come back into Clarice's voice as she began to tell me who he was.

"Dad was an engineer. He always loved to take things apart and figure out how they worked. He didn't always do that with his hands. But if something made him curious, he'd start reading or tinkering. He just had to know. Sometimes, it was almost like an obsession. But he would figure something out and move on or invent something new along the way. Whatever caught his curiosity usually came out better than it started. Oh, Western Electric, that's who he worked for. He ended up coming up with like forty-two patents in his career. A few of those were after he retired and the company broke up."

"What did he do for fun?"

Clarice chuckled. "Everything I just told you."

"What puts a smile on his face now?"

She slowly exhaled. "Samantha, my daughter. Like peas in a pod…They think the same way. He used to try to tutor her, and they fought for years till she took honors chemistry in high school. Then they just clicked, and he stopped questioning her interest in art. Now she has a master's in chemical engineering and does art restoration. He thinks it's really funny, but he's so proud of her. I can't tell you half of what she does, but he could."

Often, the most important question I ask sounds simple at face value but can be difficult to answer. The question is broad enough that it sometimes helps me catch things we missed because the answer can be anything, but it often takes us to the heart of it all.

"Tell me what you're worried about the most for your father?"

There was an auditory shudder as she inhaled and a pause that told me she was thinking. "I'm worried about his COPD. I'm worried that he's so tired. I don't want him to suffer."

I paraphrased her words back to her to be sure I'd understood her correctly. Then I told her that after seeing him, I also worried about those same concerns.

"I could only speak briefly with your father because he's working hard to breathe, and I wanted him to save his air. I was more direct with him than usual. Actually, he was more direct with me than I'm used to. One of the first things he said to me was that he wanted us to allow him to die."

Clarice's emotions steadied after giving voice to her worries. She was similarly forthright in saying, "I'm not surprised."

I shared with her that we were preparing to put together a plan in which the focus of our care would be keeping him comfortable and honoring his request to remove the mask. That mask was essentially life support, and I affirmed that Clarice understood. She also agreed we should abide by what Ernie had told us.

In the hospital culture, family is important, and we support their presence. That was particularly true with end-of-life care to the extent that even in a new pandemic, visitation would be allowed for the dying. I asked Clarice if she or other family members might be coming in to visit. The conversation suddenly became flush with new emotions. Clarice explained that Ernie's siblings were frail and on the other side of the country. Clarice herself had moderate COPD and was fearful about the risk of exposure. Her husband was immunocompromised with cancer treatment.

"There's my daughter Samantha, but I don't want her to come. I won't let her come. She's pregnant." Clarice didn't want to risk exposing others to COVID.

It seemed there would be no family visitors. We made arrangements for messages to be conveyed to Ernie and a few less-than-successful attempts at phone calls while I reported the details of my consultation to the pulmonary critical care team. Normally, we'd have a volunteer from No One Dies Alone (NODA) sit at the bedside, but volunteers, typically retirees, were also presently banned from the hospital to eliminate their exposure risk. I quietly dreaded the reality that Ernie would likely die in an empty room—no visitors, no family.

Forty-five minutes later, Samantha called. She'd spoken with her mother and was seeking details about his care transition and timing. I shared the plan I'd discussed with Clarice, the critical care team, and Ernie. We'd hang a morphine drip at a low dose and give him some Ativan. Neither of the drugs would bring about his death, which was never their purpose. The medications would reduce air hunger—the anxiety of breathlessness. We could increase the dose to target a point of comfort. Ironically, by reducing respiratory distress, sometimes breathing became less labored and more efficient.

Samantha said, "Okay, I'm coming in. I'll be there in thirty minutes."

There was nothing cavalier about Samantha. She was clearly pregnant and had her wits about her. She paid close attention to instructions regarding donning and doffing her protective equipment since close-proximity exposure was part of the risk equation. Ernie's ICU nurse assisted with all of the requisite steps, then walked her to the bedside where she took up a seat and held his hand. She spoke with him for a while, but I have no idea what was said.

The mask came off, and Sam and Ernie spent some time together with periods of dialogue and periods of silence. The medications played their part; he wasn't in distress but did tire quickly. After an hour, he was no longer conscious, and Sam decided it was time for her to leave. Ernie died peacefully sometime after midnight. He was alone but never abandoned.

Even though I'd been protected, I was wondering if I'd been exposed to COVID, so I watched for his lab results. They came back three days later.

Negative. This was not a pandemic case. COVID had not wounded his body or influenced his choices, but it had altered the way we cared for him and his family.

Introduction

First of all, thank you for purchasing this book. I hope it serves to enlighten you regarding inpatient palliative consultation and provides some humor to recharge the practice batteries of those within the field.

Healthcare is a wild world. I work in a multidisciplinary palliative medicine consult service that spans two hospitals in person and reaches three others through a growing palliative telemedicine consult service. This book will cover both the normal and challenging reasons for palliative consultation while also helping the uninitiated understand its full breadth. This is storytelling with a purpose and side order of laughter.

This work began in 2019 before the COVID-19 pandemic began to leave its mark in the lexicon of humanity. As I continue to edit, add, and delete, I'm figuring out where and how to address this topic that's been omnipresent for the better part of a year. I have little doubt that books are being written about it from many different perspectives. I will write to that topic toward the end of the book from the lens of my experience. I'll leave the detailed chronology and political failures that plagued this nation to the full critique of others with an objective focus that comes with the scope of time. Before I allow time's passage, I will write of COVID with the unfiltered, raw-skinned feel of what I'm seeing in the present.

To start, I'll describe a variety of typical palliative medicine consults and the language I might use in working with patients and families under stress. The dark humor comes from observing how often we struggle to care for one another and sometimes get it so wrong.

Early in my career, I was fortunate to observe master clinicians, and to this day, we routinely discuss cases and learn from each other's approaches. Palliative medicine, after all, is deep communication paired with clinical knowledge. Feel free to steal language in your approach to family meetings and conversation.

There is a robust and growing body of knowledge demonstrating the impact of palliative care in decision-making, patient and family coping, quality of life, and cost of care. Through advances in healthcare, people have both the blessing and curse of living through previously fatal challenges while accruing the physical degradation that comes with longevity. It is the rare victory to both live long and remain healthy. If we could envision the trajectory of a person's life who lived a few hundred years ago, it would appear very different than it does today.

In the past, life generally cruised along at a level of relatively good health with an abrupt decline toward death. Picture a capable, elderly farmer working the fields one day then developing a fever after contracting pneumonia and dying over the course of the following week. In the modern era, we treat many conditions that were historically fatal. As a result of our successes, the nature of health challenges has transitioned to a longer, gradual trajectory as we deal with the complications of chronic disease and make choices about acute interventions that have the potential to preserve life. This longer trajectory presents many with decisions deeply embedded in the complexity of healthcare.

In contrast, consider a type 1 diabetic patient in the modern era. From diagnosis, we have an opportunity for good disease management and long life expectancy in a condition that was previously fatal shortly after diagnosis. Depending on how the patient engages and responds to treatment, they may live a long and healthy life or go on to develop vascular disease, cardiac disease, kidney disease, neurologic problems, or blindness. Interventions such as bypass surgery, vascular surgery, laser eye surgery, and amputation may come up in this person's lifetime and need navigation. Diagnostic imaging and IV contrast dye may present a threat to kidney function, and late-stage questions may include deciding whether or not to engage in dialysis. This is a very different trajectory compared to pneumonia or diabetes in 1910 when insulin and antibiotics did not exist and people didn't survive to experience related morbidity.

The same diabetic patient now might be followed by a myriad of providers. While robust resources are good, decision-making can become more challenging. This diabetic patient might see an internal medicine provider, endocrinologist, cardiologist, vascular surgeon, neurologist, gastroenterologist, ophthalmologist, and nephrologist, to name a few. When decision-making or symptom management becomes particularly complex, which of these providers helps to pull the picture together and clarify goals of care? In reality, every team member could try to engage in this task. The fast-paced, often fragmented, time-constricted nature of our healthcare system makes a deep-dive holistic approach to healthcare difficult at best. This complex navigation is often akin to assembling a jigsaw puzzle while riding a rollercoaster. Symptom management and navigating complex decision-making happens to be part of specialties such as palliative care or the narrative medicine approach.

What effect does a good palliative care encounter have to offer? Research shows us that families highly value honesty and being informed of anticipated patient outcomes or status changes.[4] It shouldn't come as a surprise that patients and families who are less informed suffer for it. Del Gaudio et al. (2011) found that families with poor communication and teamwork have higher psychologic morbidity.[5] The act of counseling can be beneficial by enlightening family communication dynamics and serve as a therapeutic intervention. Doing this well also includes assessing who needs information and with what level of detail. Palliative medicine consultations are associated with improved patient and family

---

[4] P Hudson et al., "Family Meetings in Palliative Care: Are They Effective?," *Palliative Medicine* 23, no. 2 (2009): 150–157, https://doi.org/10.1177/0269216308099960

[5] Francesca Del Gaudio et al., "Challenges in Providing Family-Centered Support to Families in Palliative Care," *Palliative Medicine* 26, no. 8 (October 2011): 1025–1033, https://doi.org/10.1177/0269216311426919

assessment of quality of life in the setting of complex, life-limiting illnesses.[6]

It's also worth noting that inpatient palliative care consultation enriches the patient and family's knowledge base, which in turn impacts their capacity to make decisions.[7] This is of notable importance when we recall the number of constantly changing providers and voices involved in each person's healthcare. To say that some days it takes a village might be an understatement. Healthcare is sometimes a group of migrant workers that changes with shifts, days of the week, disciplines, and locations. Many patients have more than five disciplines involved, seeing three or more clinicians in each while also being seen in two to three hospital networks over the course of a year. Doing a quick calculation, there might be forty-five different doctors, physician assistants (PA), nurse practitioners (NP), and other specialists involved. Each of the patient's family members may hear a completely different story. Somebody needs to periodically pull the branches of the story together to ensure it makes sense.

The family meeting is often the most valuable tool in the palliative care toolbox precisely because of the fragmented and overwhelming nature of acute care. I wouldn't ask you to simply take my word for it as the body of evidence continues to grow. Let's briefly touch on this. Boyle et al. did a systematic review of the literature, finding, "An early, proactive multidisciplinary family meeting should be held for each ICU patient who is admitted who is at significant risk for death, prolonged stay, or decisional conflict."[8] Families consistently rated communication with clinicians as a top

---

[6] Jennifer S. Temel et al., "Early Palliative Care for Patients with Metastatic Non–Small-Cell Lung Cancer," *New England Journal of Medicine* 363, no. 8 (2010): 733-742, https://doi.org/10.1056/nejmoa1000678

[7] Susan Enguidanos et al., "Family Members' Perceptions of Inpatient Palliative Care Consult Services: A Qualitative Study," *Palliative Medicine* 28, no. 1 (June 2013): 42-48, https://doi.org/10.1177/0269216313491620

[8] D. K. Boyle, P. A. Miller, and S. A. Forbes-Thompson, "Communications and End-of-Life Care in the Intensive Care Unit," *Critical Care Nursing Quarterly* 28, no. 4 (2005): 311.

priority, and multidisciplinary teams were among the most successful at meeting this need.[9] Later reviews of the literature also yielded similar support for family meetings. Sullivan et al. found a potential for reduced patient and family suffering, improved satisfaction, enhanced psychologic well-being, and improved decision-making surrounding medical interventions as a product of family meetings.[10]

While simultaneously improving quality of life, palliative medicine is also associated with informed selections of healthcare choices that reduce the cost of the care provided.[11] One of the ways this occurs is the empowered and informed patient often makes decisions that influence their time receiving critical care. One study explored the length of intensive care unit (ICU) stay with early palliative care intervention. While patients in the early consultation group had a shorter length of ICU stay (8.96 versus 16.28 days), they showed no difference in the total length of hospitalization, mortality rate, or discharge disposition.[12] It begs the question, does the fully informed patient better understand what healthcare choices are truly in their best interests?

Early palliative consultation is also associated with improved patient quality of life and reductions in healthcare cost.[13] This is an important observation when practicing in the world's most expensive healthcare system. The specifics of these savings were explored in some detail by Dr. Morrison and his colleagues. In 2008, they published a data analysis for 21,077 patients in New York,

---

[9] Ibid., 302–316.

[10] S. S. Sullivan, C. Ferreira da rosa Silva, and M. A. Meeker, "Family Meetings at End of Life: A Systematic Review," *Journal of Hospice and Palliative Nursing* 17, no. 3 (2015): 196-205, https://doi.org/10.107/NJH.0000000000000147

[11] R. Sean Morrison et al., "Palliative Care Consultation Teams Cut Hospital Costs For Medicaid Beneficiaries," *Health Affairs* 30, no. 3 (2011): 454-463, https://doi.org/10.1377/hlthaff.2010.0929

[12] Ibid.

[13] Morrison et al., "Palliative Care Consultation Teams Cut Hospital Costs for Medicaid Beneficiaries," 454–463.

comparing the cost for patients receiving palliative care versus those receiving standard care alone. In this matched group, they found a net cost savings of $1,696 per admission. Remember that palliative care can be, and often is, combined with curative and life-sustaining treatment. When it was involved at the end of life, the savings were greater at $4,908.[14]

To provide more evidence, Morrison and his colleagues decided to take a further look at the cost of care, looking at admissions between 2004 and 2007, again in New York. As care gets more expensive, it seems the savings associated with palliative care gains value. Patients were matched to a group receiving usual care. For patients receiving palliative care who were discharged alive, a $4,098 cost per admission savings was noted ($p = 0.04$).[15] Similar to the earlier study, patients with this care during their last hospital stay were found to have the greatest cost savings at $7,563. The researchers utilized these findings to project what state-wide cost savings might be annually if 2 to 6 percent of hospitalized Medicaid patients received palliative care. This estimate was between 84 million and 252 million dollars per year.[16] For a moment, just imagine the potential savings in 2020 with a 6 percent palliative care engagement across the nation's Medicare population. Palliative care is good care for those with complex, life-limiting illnesses and has billions of dollars in savings potential.

Let's take this line of thought a bit further. What if we provided the high value, quality of life improving care to the complex, life-limiting illness population earlier in the hospital stay? Does this have further cost savings? It seems that it does. May et al. conducted a prospective observational study at five hospital centers focused on 3,218 English-speaking patients with a cancer diagnosis between

---

[14] R. Sean Morrison et al., "Cost Savings Associated with US Hospital Palliative Care Consultation Programs," *Archives of Internal Medicine* 168 (August 2008): 1783–1790.

[15] Morrison et al., "Palliative care Consultation Teams Cut Hospital Costs for Medicaid Beneficiaries," 454–463.

[16] Ibid.

2007 and 2011.[17] This study explored whether the timing of a palliative care team consultation resulted in a difference in direct cost savings. They compared a usual care group to those with a specialist-led palliative medicine team. Patients were matched based on disease severity. May et al. found there was a cost savings associated with earlier palliative care consultative intervention.[18] A 14 percent cost reduction, $1,312, was observed if consultation occurred by day six of the hospital course ($p = 0.04$). A greater cost reduction of 24 percent, or $2,280, was observed for patients receiving consultation within two days of admission ($p < 0.001$).[19]

A fascinating point of contrast exists if we consider the cost of bringing a cancer drug to the US market. Targets of this pursuit could include a cure, mitigation of disease progression, reduced burdens from side effects, or very often something as narrow as a few additional weeks of life. The literature shows a huge range in the estimated cost of bringing a drug to market.

DiMasi, Grabowski, and Hansen (2016) looked at a randomly selected group of 106 new drugs to form an estimate for the cost of an approved compound.[20] When they factored in abandoned compounds, the average cost for a new drug was $1.395 billion dollars in the 2013 economy. If a company also invests in marketing, the amount escalates to an average of $2.558 billion dollars. In comparison to drug development, expert-level palliative care requires training, experience, and personnel without seven and a half years of research and development or marketing expenses.

---

[17] Peter May et al., "Prospective Cohort Study of Hospital Palliative Care Teams for Inpatients with Advanced Cancer: Earlier Consultation Is Associated with Larger Cost-Saving Effect," *Journal of Clinical Oncology* 33, no. 25 (January 2015): 2745-2752, https://doi.org/10.1200/jco.2014.60.2334

[18] Ibid.

[19] Ibid.

[20] Joseph A. DiMasi, Henry G. Grabowski, and Ronald W. Hansen, "Innovation in the Pharmaceutical Industry: New Estimates of R&D Costs," *Journal of Health Economics* 47 (2016): 20-33, https://doi.org/10.1016/j.jhealeco.2016.01.012

So, how does palliative care combined with cancer care relate to the benchmarks of life expectancy and quality of life? Fortunately for us, Temel and colleagues look at this in a landmark study published in 2010 where they compared standard cancer care for patients with non-small cell lung cancer to standard care in addition to regular involvement from a palliative care team. Palliative care clinician support began at the time of diagnosis, three weeks into the hospital stay, or in a month. Prognostic factors were matched, and the researchers looked at two main points: longevity and quality of life.

The researchers found the experimental group had fewer depressive symptoms ($p = 0.01$) and a higher quality of life ($p = 0.03$). At the end of life, patients in the palliative care group elected to receive less aggressive care (cardiopulmonary resuscitation, chemotherapy) than those in the control group: 33 percent versus 54 percent ($p = 0.05$). The landmark finding in the study revealed that despite electing less aggressive end-of-life care, the palliative care group exhibited longer survival rates and a higher quality of life than the oncology-only group ($p = 0.02$).[21] Not bad for a widely applicable skilled intervention that didn't involve a billion dollars in research and development.

Palliative consultation has not been associated with a shorter life expectancy, but rather, the opposite. But as more patients are living longer with complex illnesses, there's a growing need for open conversations to establish goals of care. It's this role that is often viewed as the hallmark of palliative medicine. Ongoing research continues to gather data on the cost-saving effect of palliative support's early engagement in the care of patients and families, and there's strong evidence supporting the value of coordinated family meetings. The data supports a reduction in family and patient psychologic morbidity in addition to the improved quality of life (Del Gaudio et al., 2011).[22] These findings validate the work of palliative medicine specialists on an ethical and financial level

---

[21] May et al., "Prospective Cohort Study," 2745–2752.

[22] Del Gaudio et al., "Challenges in Providing Family-Centered Support," 1025–1033.

The Journey to Palliative Medicine

I need to talk a little bit about personal style. It should come as little surprise that personality comes in a wide variety of forms. This book isn't meant to be firmly prescriptive in how you must deal with language, families, patients, or specific issues. Having a natural approach at the bedside is an important and necessary ingredient in the sincerity we bring to the care we provide. The hope is that with time and practice, you'll be able to incorporate valuable elements into your style. This is meant to include both context and cadence—a surprisingly important and beguiling aspect for many clinicians. Early in my palliative career, I was taught that 70 percent of a good palliative care consult is listening. We can do a great deal of good or harm depending on how well we listen and what we do with the other 30 percent of our time.

Since we're talking a little bit about style, it may be of use to you to understand some of my background, influences, and ethical considerations in practice. Basically, how did I choose this work and develop this sense of purpose? Each of our life stories and clinical exposures influence how we approach the challenging psychosocial dynamics of practice. Having an awareness of our own background may help serve us in recognizing our own biases and restrain or exploit them when needed.

I've been a nurse since 1996 and received my education in a small liberal arts college in Pennsylvania.

I was raised by a teacher and a chaplain who emigrated from South Africa. I grew up hearing stories of families in crisis, spiritual distress, and moments of grace from my father while receiving invaluable, pragmatic direction from my mother. Being a type 1 diabetic also gave me early exposure to the healthcare world and influenced my dive into the system.

I entered college the year after high school. During my undergraduate education, we periodically talked about the challenge of transitioning from education to practice. I did the best I could and spent the summer after my junior year getting extra training on an orthopedic surgical floor. I picked up new skills and gained a great deal of confidence which I carried into my senior year, though I wasn't under the illusion that entry into practice would be easy. My first job out of undergraduate was at a small hospital in Maryland, and the transition into the graduate nurse (GN) position at this old hospital was a shock to me despite my preparation for a challenge. The patient load was high, staffing short, and pace relentless. This was further compounded by the capricious variation of shift work. We were at a time when generations were moving from an authoritarian patriarchal care approach to a patient-directed philosophy. Each institution also had its own culture, influencing how care was provided. During that first year, I witnessed some of the worst use of language in my career. My fellow graduates and I shared the observation that this was a place to both learn what to do and what not to do in practice.

There were characters both among the staff as well as the patient population we served. We did what we could to cobble together effective care for our patients. I could speak of many interesting patients in this small hospital.

One particular character was a shirtless, skeletal, wrinkled, end-stage COPD patient seated in a tripod position shouting to his doctor, "I'm going to die today!"

His doctor replied, "What?"

"I'm going to *die* today!"

"What?"

Dr. W., who was in his late seventies to early eighties, couldn't hear what was being yelled to him from twelve feet away, and even though his patient was over a decade younger, he looked a decade older. Suddenly, I found myself in a geriatric translation between the two of them.

"He says he's going to die today!" I repeated the exchange with increased volume two more times before the esteemed senior physician grasped the words.

Dr. W., upon hearing the sentence, looked at the patient and said, "Go ahead, try it. You won't like it." He turned and walked farther down the hall.

There was no discussion of patient goals or end-stage progression of COPD. It wasn't part of the culture to address these issues. Admitting, treating, rinsing, and repeating was what gained revenue and remains the approach in much of the United States.

I don't recall this patient dying that day. Dr. W., however, did die a few months later, but not as a patient or after retirement. He passed away on duty in the cafeteria over his oatmeal breakfast. His son, also a doctor, followed up with his father's patients after rounds and double-checked his father's 1960s-era approach in the latter phase of his career. I'd like to believe there was a quiet understanding of the dignity in his need to work.

In my early days, I learned skills like placing IVs and running interference for distraught families while in the company of thick-skinned veteran nurses with a capacity for compassion, good care, and damage repair. I became efficient at rapidly moving massive amounts of medications while navigating through family questions about the impact of advancing disease. I saw few people taking the time to have deep conversations about patient goals or disease progress, instead using more reactionary caring. I also knew of staff who placed IVs on each other and wore oxygen masks to lighten hangovers during the workday. In retrospect, much of what I learned were efficiency skills mixed with lessons about how to avoid time-consuming conversations. In all honesty, some of those first career lessons almost broke my will to practice.

Ellen

A few months later I was providing meds and flushing Ellen's IV while she apprehensively awaited the results of her clinical workup. Earlier in the day, she'd asked me to call and request an update about her biopsy. Her attending physician was a quick-moving female in her late fifties who'd been dubbed the "Ice Queen" by members of the staff. The Ice Queen arrived at the patient's door but didn't cross the threshold.

"Your test results are back."

Those five words were enough to stop all movement in the room. I swear even the beeping IV held its silence longer in suspend mode. A statement of gravity and threat of mortality hinged on the weight of the next sentence. Its delivery would make a powerful impression. The Ice Queen still didn't enter the room, instead making a subtle shift to her left—I thought, perhaps, to lean on the door frame.

"You have cancer."

She gave a subtle nod of the head and a curt parting statement of "Have a good day." With that, the Ice Queen furthered her shift to the left and exited the door frame, moving out of sight. There was no warning shot, no exchange of words, no plan for a follow-up, no effort to lessen or acknowledge the shock. The verbal grenade exploded in the room, and both Ellen and I were deaf in the silence that followed.

The IV pump began its beeping protest anew. I soon found myself receiving every question I wasn't equipped to answer.

"How bad is the cancer? Is there a treatment? Am I going to die? How will I tell my family? What does this mean? Could the test be wrong?"

Much later, many of those answers came in the form of an oncology consult, but Ellen was clearly damaged by this cold approach.

Russel

Befuddled care didn't always come from poor communication as much as total lack of it. Russel was a Vietnam vet sent over from across the river for treatment of suspected pneumonia in the setting of his COPD. (Across the river is a medical center which treats a broad number of concerns such as mental health, including Russel's schizophrenia.) Russel was promptly started on antibiotics, but in the geographic shift from the psychiatric care to our hospital, his plan didn't include the continuation of his psychiatric meds. The attending physician didn't have time to sort through all of his records and was more comfortable treating just his pneumonia. In that day and age, electronic medical records were still in their infancy and didn't yet transfer between institutions.

On day one, Russel was a compliant, sociable, and generally a likeable guy. On day two, he was still taking his antibiotics when you could find him between perpetual smoke breaks. He was the kind of patient you wanted to have as he was relatively healthy—aside from the pneumonia—and rarely needed anything. On day three, he needed a bit more encouragement to come in from the October cold, especially because he was wearing just a thin hospital gown, but he was still pleasant and accepting of care. Most of the time, he was getting his antihypertensive medications and antibiotics, though it was hit and miss.

By day four, without his routine psychiatric medications, things began to noticeably deteriorate. Instead of simply watching the TV between smoke runs, he began talking to it. The next afternoon, they observed him casually sauntering down the hallway in all his naked glory.

"Yo, brother! Put some clothes on," yelled a fellow patient. Ever docile and compliant, Russel ambled back and put his clothes on, and we put his IV back in. Between his minimally dressed outdoor state and constant smoking, I'm not sure we were improving upon his pneumonia much less his overall state of health.

The next morning, he managed to leave the floor and dispense with the now-optional clothing. The ramifications of this would have some bearing on where his legs took him. The smoking area, while perhaps exciting, was not a crisis. The cafeteria would of course have a rapt audience. If he went to another unit, some confusion and redirection would occur.

Instead, he sauntered straight into the operating room (OR) during an active surgery and without a thread of clothing. The casual observer instantly became the observed.

His pneumonia was promptly announced cured, and I was tasked as being part of the security/nurse detail driving him back to the medical center. The fear was that he might try to exit the security vehicle on the I-95 bridge eighty feet over the Susquehanna River. Aside from his persistent cough, though, he was a model passenger.

Transition Period

In the course of that year, we were on our third nurse manager, and I was seriously questioning my career choices. I was also getting paid the exact same salary I'd made sitting by the sunny poolside as a lifeguard the summer before. The hospital somehow didn't cover my insulin pump supplies, so I stayed on my parents' benefits and chose to double my salary by going per diem without work benefits. The hospital needed me full time regardless of the pay change, so the net result was a considerable pay raise.

I'd heard enough stories about the charge nurse using oxygen on some mornings to sober up and the illicit affairs of the medical staff. I'd seen aged physicians ordering glucose checks by venipuncture instead of glucometer. I witnessed many examples of procedural "care" without attention to quality.

It was time to leave, one way or another.

I followed the nurses who left before me and arrived at a hospital to the north in Delaware. The difference between the non-teaching, roughly 180-bed hospital to a new state-of-the-art teaching institution with 900 beds can't be easily overstated. It was perhaps the best choice of my young career, representing a salvation from the worst of what I saw during my first year while also appreciating the hard-earned skills I brought to the bedside. The hospital was reasonably staffed, and the nurses were empowered to advocate for their patients. The institution itself was a vital and growing place, rich with people bringing new ideas forward.

Milton

I spent the next three years on a surgical floor and began to fill some veteran staff roles. I learned how to explain advanced illness and to advocate more effectively for patients. At that point, patients wore wristbands with identifying information. This was prior to the use of bar code scanning for medication administration. The bands denoted identity, fall risk, allergies, no venipuncture, and most importantly, code status. I witnessed and began to learn from discussions whether a patient at certain stages in their life would be accepting of heroic measures such as CPR and breathing tubes. We exchanged this information at the end of shifts, but the bands served as a quick reference in emergencies.

One Saturday afternoon, I received Milton back on the fifth floor where I worked. He'd been discharged the day before and was returning to us from the nursing home in a fair degree of respiratory distress. In fact, he'd been gone so briefly that he still wore all of his hospital bands. I took note of the yellow do-not-resuscitate (DNR) band before we had him in bed. His wife, Agnes, was more able-bodied and arrived shortly after her eighty-eight-year-old husband, following him up from the emergency department.

Milt's oxygen saturation range was in numbers lower than his age, and he was breathing quite rapidly despite the oxygen I'd applied. He was using accessory muscles and no longer cognizant of the clinical buzz surrounding him. The admitting physician sent over the admission orders which also noted "full code," meaning that aggressive interventions such as the chest compressions of CPR and the insertion of a breathing tube would be utilized to delay death. I checked with Agnes and voiced my concern that her husband appeared to be dying.

Agnes was both doting and astute. "He's been dying for a while now. I just want to be with him and see him go peacefully."

There was an imminent discord between the code status orders, his band, and the wishes stated by his spouse of over sixty years.

I called the attending physician in an attempt to reconcile these concerns and was told that he wouldn't change the code status until he physically saw the patient. He made it clear that it might be a few hours as he'd just left Milt's part of the hospital, positing that the band was invalid as it was placed before he was sent here for a "higher level of care." The higher level of care Agnes wanted for her husband couldn't have been more different than what his attending physician envisioned.

Once off the phone, I met with Agnes and other nurses from the floor. We all understood that the idea of coding this frail and dying man was more akin to assault than medical care, especially thanks to Agnes's words and the band.

Agnes asked, "What should I do?"

The thought of her having to stand in the doorway to physically fend off the rush of a code team was not a sight I wanted to see. We decided to call the code team directly—but outside the paging system—and have a direct negotiation before his breathing failed and heart stopped. They came, met with Agnes, and saw Milton in person. The ICU attending changed the code status on the spot.

Milt died with his wife at his side long before the attending made it to the bedside. Agnes didn't have to bar the door from the code team, and we didn't assault Milt's body, though we could've done a far better job treating his respiratory distress at an earlier point. It was a partial but important win in fighting for my patients. I say that in plural because, though Agnes was not a patient, we cared for her at that time too.

When my opportunity for growth there flattened, I progressed to the same medical ICU that tended to Milt and eventually joined the code team.

The ICU gradually became a new home where I encountered a different set of characters over the next three years. The daily work focused on my two patients, allowing me to incur a deeper knowledge of their clinical problems and their families.

With the often-demanding nature of my team members, I came to understand the phrase "nurses eat their young" while also being challenged to grow professionally. I worked with some amazing and some challenging people. I took on students and often skipped lunch.

Over time, I grew more confident in my own skills and capable of filling in the information blanks for patients or, more commonly, their families. I often found myself being asked for my opinion and entrusted with the fears and wishes of those I cared for. On the better days, I'd be within a team who would hear my relaying of those concerns and respond to my request for a family meeting. On the bad days, I could see all the disconnected dots a family might need to navigate complex decisions but not be in the clinical role to voice that information or put the patient and family's desires into action. In the bedside role, I also had less clinical gravitas to help families navigate chronic critical illness. In those circumstances, the work, despite the best of intent, was sometimes serving to prolong suffering or override free will than to truly serve the patient.

What follows is a story where the team got the dialogue right in the most difficult of circumstances.

Singing the Gate Open

The emotional spectrum at the end of life is broad, from heart-wrenching to surprisingly fulfilling and uplifting. This story is a rich mix of emotional content and family strength that has continued to reverberate in my mind for the past twenty years.

In 2001, I practiced as a bedside registered nurse (RN) in a twelve-bed critical care unit in Delaware. We had just adopted a bedside documentation platform that permitted us to be a bit more present in the room with patients and their families.

I was caring for a forty-seven-year-old woman named Valentina. She was a moderately obese African American woman who wore a smile on her warm face in an attempt to mask her growing panic. While she was partway through a long trip with extended family from North Carolina to New York, she began experiencing increased difficulty in breathing. The family convoy had pulled off the interstate to get some assistance. She was alert and communicative but required escalating levels of oxygen support in a short amount of time. What everyone had hoped would be a particularly bad asthma attack proved to be a massive saddle pulmonary embolism (PE). The PE was steadily showering clots to both lungs, robbing her of the ability to absorb oxygen.

Valentina, her three well-dressed towering brothers, and one female cousin were quickly briefed by our ICU intensivist. During their bedside discussion, the patient became acutely hypoxic and was intubated. We elected not to heavily sedate her as the family continued to communicate with her and mitigate her distress.

Thrombolytic drugs were not having the desired effect of alleviating her respiratory failure, and the critical care team began to run out of viable rescue options. Through a bridge of trust and honest communication, her family quickly developed an understanding of what was happening. Death was coming—unfairly, rapidly, and in plain sight.

Valentina destabilized so precipitously that endovascular clot retrieval after thrombolysis was not an option. The family maintained their presence and made the decision to abstain from CPR as it wouldn't address the underlying problem, no matter how young and otherwise healthy she was. They wanted to spend the remaining time with her, and visitor limitations were dispensed with. Valentina was the youngest patient on the unit, and the events of the day had struck with the randomness of lightning from a clear sky.

I provided small doses of IV morphine and Ativan to reduce her panic along with 100 percent oxygen through her ventilator. Valentina stayed mostly alert with her brothers holding her hand and speaking to her of family events. The matriarch of the family and an uncle joined us, and she even curved the occasional smile around her endotracheal tube.

It had been a long and heavy morning. Over the next forty-five minutes, her oxygen saturation began to drift below 70 percent, and consciousness fluctuated further.

The hospital staff was tense. We liked to be busy, to have a sense of purpose or a tool to fight back with when death was coming. This sense was even more intense when the patient was young and death felt unnatural. In moments like that, we needed some sense of action as an emotional defense. To acknowledge there was nothing we could do felt like failure. I felt unshielded, and each of us attempted to show compassion in our own way. Food for family; pastoral care for the spirit; pacing, fidgeting, deep breaths, checking the chart repeatedly.

It was around this difficult point that the purpose of their trip became apparent in a spontaneous and powerful way. While standing at the bedside with their backs to the half-open door, one brother began to sing. What came out was the deep baritone of a heartfelt gospel song. Moments later, Valentina's other two brothers and cousin joined in. The family was traveling as part of a gospel music group, singing with other congregations.

They filled the ICU room from corner to corner with the warm rhythm of their sound. I could feel the vibrations of their singing within my chest as I sat down by the computer. The sound penetrated the folds of fabric in the bed and filled every space in the room. Valentina's eyes fluttered open but without the look of fear that had been there before.

My colleagues and I shifted from trying to be busy to simply being present with this family. I stopped trying to chart while seated at the foot of the bed in the corner of the room. I could barely make out the screen anymore, and there would never be a checkbox for that kind of grace.

The family continued to sing one song to the next. Word spread through the ICU corridor about the reason for the live gospel music echoing through the halls. Other families passed by the door and nodded in respect and understanding.

Valentina's pulse oximetry probe lost its wave form about ten minutes after the singing began. She was no longer initiating breaths, but her heart monitor registered a rhythm that might have been pulseless. As the tempo in the final gospel song climbed up and stepped back down, it was matched perfectly by the remaining waves on Valentina's heart monitor. I watched as her heart rhythm danced in tandem throughout the entire song. As it finished, there was only a flat line on the monitor.

The gospel-singing family sang her through the gates to heaven, and when they stopped for a moment, the silence was a crushing vacuum.

To this day, I still carry a piece of that rhythm within my heart, and it's one of the most powerful moments of grace that I've seen.

Leaving the ICU

During this three-year period, I spent some time trying to give back to those pursuing a nursing degree by taking adjunct faculty positions at two different community colleges. I also returned to being a student myself and earned my masters in an executive practice track. I thoroughly enjoyed the clinical rotations with my students while sharing the challenge of learning with future colleagues. Despite these steps, I came to realize that administration or full-time teaching wasn't where I needed to be. I enjoyed the critical care world but felt an unceasing sense of frustration and need to challenge myself. The next career leap was one that was formative and challenged me in ways I'd never been before.

During my time in the ICU, we periodically had patients with an acute brain injury. This might've been present in the form of a devastating stoke or profound damage from lack of oxygen following cardiac arrest. Two things often followed these types of stories: determining if the patient can survive and discussing what components of their whole person will be intact. These difficult conversations are often filled with the threat of uncertainty. Family meetings with neurology or neurosurgery can be intense and come with a mix of hope and despair, varying with prognosis and the families' capacity to assimilate information.

The most intense cases are the ones where we recognize that the injury isn't survivable—more specifically, the cases where the patient's neurologic exam is consistent with brain death. Initial examination consistent with brain death is an observational point that triggers a methodical analysis to determine if the patient is indeed brain dead.

Each hospital has a protocol for collaborative analysis, examination, and confirmatory testing by two or more clinicians. If a patient is determined to be brain dead, they've met the legally established criteria and are irrevocably dead. We often see the media or the lay person euphemistically use this term in describing an injury, a vegetative state, or sometimes even common stupidity. In reality, brain death is quite final and scrupulously assessed before being determined.

Explaining this is emotional for both the family members receiving the news and the clinician giving it. Unlike other health conditions, brain death isn't always preceded by a disease or illness to warn us death is coming. Now, imagine for a moment delivering this same news to a family, perhaps distrustful, with limited understanding of medical care and the vulnerabilities of the human brain. Pair this with a family who's observing the rise and fall of their loved one's chest with the support of a ventilator. That person might have warm hands, a pink face, a palpable heartbeat, and a visible rhythm on the same monitor, yet they're dead. Multiple specialist clinicians will perform evaluations separated by spans of time to confirm brain death. These patients are without pupillary response to light, corneal response to touch, ocular movement to the cold caloric test, cough to deep endotracheal suctioning, gag with manipulation of the endotracheal tube, withdrawal from painful stimuli, blood flow to the brain on vascular imaging, or a single solitary breath on a minutes-long apnea test in the absence of sedation. Imaging may even show that under the pressure of edema, the patient's brain has herniated through the base of the skull. A time of death is documented with the second confirmatory brain death exam. Despite this thoroughness, in the absence of good communication, the patient may look and be perceived to be very much alive.

I witnessed skilled critical care providers gradually inform families that they suspected their loved one might be brain dead. The slow breaking of the news allows families to hope they're wrong and rage against the apparent reality while preparing for the worst. Some families disseminate this suspicion to distant relatives and ask appropriate forward-looking questions. To complicate circumstances, an emotionally exhausted family might begin to believe they see movement of the shoulders with the mechanical control of the ventilator and struggle to reconcile hope with reality.

When this type of death is determined, there should be no decisions for a family to make regarding removing the deceased from the ventilator. The visitation of nearby family or a spiritual leader might be waited for while we remain as attentive as possible to their emotional needs. Beyond these steps, we don't ask them to make any medical decisions. With the declaration of brain death, the stark reality is that death has come, and the dead of the hospital reside in the morgue, not the ICU. There is one exception to that rule.

When the ICU team begins to suspect impending or present brain death in a patient, there are legal and ethical obligations to reach out to a specialized team with a very different role and set of skills. In Delaware, that team is the Gift of Life Donor Program (GOL). Organ donation is a possibility in approximately 1 to 2 percent of all hospital deaths. Brain deaths represent the highest likelihood of viable organs capable of saving the lives of as many as eight people. The need is substantial. As of 2017 there are 114,000 Americans awaiting organ transplant, and twenty of them die daily.[23]

So, in these cases, we place a call to GOL, and often within an hour, an organ transplant coordinator will quietly show up. While we, the ICU team, work hard to preserve a life hanging in the balance, the coordinator reviews the patient's history and organ function in the background. Sometimes, they are there at the family's request and will be visible but deferential to the ICU team. There's a clear boundary over which a coordinator doesn't cross uninvited prior to declaration of brain death.

The lay public should take solace in knowing that the critical care team will actually work its hardest to maintain good hemodynamics despite a perception of futility because it's both their job and doing it well best preserves the possibility of viable organ donation.

These were the most intensive ICU cases in terms of clinical management, diagnostics, and family support.

---

[23] "Information about Organ, Eye, and Tissue Donation," Organ Donor, Organ Donor, accessed May 7, 2021, https://www.organdonor.gov/

I remember walking into my manager's office with a letter of resignation in hand. She was a veteran nurse nearing retirement who no longer practiced clinically. There was a look of surprise when the conversation led to what I was setting for next after leaving the ICU. She'd assumed that with my past teaching experience I was moving to a new faculty position. But I needed a new challenge. Gift of Life organ transplant coordinator was a new title, and during that interview, something I viewed as a new challenge beyond the walls of the current hospital.

Transplant

Upon joining GOL, we began an intensive three-month training program that included receiving didactic clinical review from experienced coordinators, attending organizational rounds, and hearing case stories. We participated in role playing that detailed the challenges and approaches in meeting families in crisis as well as dealing with professional conflict. Keep in mind, Philadelphia-based GOL coordinators can be called upon to evaluate a potential organ donor at any hospital in Delaware, the eastern half of Pennsylvania, and most of New Jersey. We could also be called to fly with a surgical team anywhere in the country if an organ were allocated to a transplant hospital in our region. Some of the large transplant hospitals might have multiple potential donors on the same day and thousands of waiting recipients. On the other hand, some smaller hospitals may have never had a potential organ donor and no relevant experience in working with a coordinator, determining brain death, or clinical management.

I fully committed myself to the learning process. I worked alongside a group of phenomenal people who regularly challenged me to use appropriate language and understand it as both verbal and physical communication. I incorporated many of the skills modeled for me then and continue to use them now. One example is the simple act of being at eye level and how that viewpoint changes dialogue. Crouching at the bedside, sitting on a trash can, or meeting more formally at a conference room table are easily overlooked but do send the critical message of engagement and time commitment.

This is the opposite of leaning in a door frame, delivering a message, and then shifting out of view.

I sold my car after orientation and was provided with a company car—coordinators were road warriors as well as clinicians. Honda Accords were reasonably fuel efficient, inconspicuous, utilitarian, and held up well with the occasional sleep-deprived car crash. The trunk was suited for the sixty pounds of gear many of us carried: Human Lymphocyte Antigen (HLA) lab kits, paper charts, spare scrubs, Red Bull, food, etc. Many of us taped a printed sign in the back window saying "Organ Transplant Coordinator." This did get my colleagues and I out of some tickets and occasionally helped with parking access. Despite those perks, it didn't take me long to begin to understand why the training program for the coordinators was so well organized and intensive. The work was critically important, and turnover was massive. The job was a brutal love-hate relationship, and I held on with both hands.

My primary mentor was a remarkable woman named Cheryl. As I approached the end of orientation, she began to shift the family dialogue and more of the organ allocation work to me, a process that often began at seven or eight in the morning and, if circumstances aligned, would normally bring us into the operating room at about two the following morning. The OR case would wrap up around 10:00 a.m., often hundreds of miles from home.

I learned to start with the social questions long before transplant consent questions when meeting a family. Sometimes, there was a large loving family that would regale you with details of a rich, well-lived life. I would hear the stories of how the patient had engaged in the world and cared for others. I would learn what hobbies and flaws made them who they were. It was typically after having this background information that we would shift the conversation to their understanding of the patient's clinical status. In some cases, they looked into the eyes of their loved one and saw the empty dilated unresponsiveness, understanding their loved one had left the body behind. Other times, we struggled to find any family for Jane or John Doe. With one man found in a casino bathroom without a wallet, the only clue we had was a dental appointment reminder card.

In many cases, we repeated the news of death and helped them really hear its finality. Once that news began to sink in, I could then begin to explore the option of organ and tissue donation. Sometimes a driver's license indicated the person's values on the subject, and we presented it to the family prescriptively. Other times, there was no clear indication, and we explored the option as it related to the values of the individual I was just coming to know. It was the most difficult time imaginable to have these conversations, but it was also the only time.

Each of their stories affected me. We were instilled with the mandate of "being the custodian of the gift." This meant honoring the potential lives saved by organ and tissue donation while caring for the family in crisis, but my bias was strongly with the donor family as I didn't work with or know the transplant recipients. Even so, the gift of donation is sacrosanct. It very often included caring for the staff members involved as well because these cases were not easy—emotionally or clinically.

Sandra

One pivotal lesson in a twenty-hour-long case was when we took Sandra to the OR for recovery of her kidneys, liver, and tissue. Sandra was in her late fifties, obese, and had a few tattoos. Her donation story began the day before. Cheryl and I were called in to relieve the starting coordinator in the hours leading to the operating room. The combined team had been through declaration of brain death and consent discussions with the family before organ allocation and surgical team assembly. OR culture is fast moving, organized, and hierarchical in nature. An organ transplant coordinator is an outsider who challenges the taboo that "nobody dies in the OR." Sandra arrived in the operating room accompanied by me, her ICU nurse, Cheryl, transport, and a respiratory therapist. She was as much a stranger to the OR team as I was that night.

Her body was transitioned to the surgical table, and the normal work banter continued throughout the room. Cheryl updated the recipient teams on labs and reviewed management details with anesthesia. It was business as usual to a point. In most ORs, there's music as the teams work. It's simply part of the culture and helps people focus while remaining agile in long cases. At that 2:00 a.m. hour, the on-call team had chosen what could best be described as heavy metal acid rock.

A body was prepped and draped on the table. The paperwork had been checked with most t's crossed and i's dotted. In all of the functional hubbub, we'd remembered most things and were nearing the time of incision. People moved about, and the angry music pumped along.

Cheryl realized that we'd all forgotten something very important: There was a body on the table, but we'd lost sight of Sandra.

There we were, strangers in an OR, coordinating a case where we didn't know the staff or wield the almighty scalpel. What Cheryl did next showed me a very different kind of power. She calmly walked over to the spewing radio next to the anesthesiologist and turned it off! Immediately, everything stopped, and attention shifted to the stranger at the head of the table. Cheryl had had the insane audacity to turn off the music and completely halt the operative machine.

She raised her head and panned the room, making eye contact with everyone as she began to speak.

With a calm, even voice, she said, "I'd like to introduce you to Sandra Elise Acevedo. She's fifty-seven years old and has two nieces, Clara and Sophia, whom she helps raise. She has a dachshund named Henry and enjoys craft work. She works at Michael's craft store and volunteers with special needs children. Today, she's going to improve the lives of many through tissue donation and save the lives of three through organ donation. I'd like to thank all of you for helping make this gift possible."

It was quiet as she turned to the radio and adjusted the volume before turning it back on. In a few seconds, she had reset the entire room.

We found Sandra.

Learning to Listen and Ask

I learned that you'd be surprised what you can get by asking. Rick, the VP of GOL, made this statement more than once, and it repeatedly proved true. Once, Cheryl was even able to redirect air traffic at an international airport to prioritize an arriving organ. A different coordinator managed to get a police escort to transport kidneys faster. But asking wasn't always easy. A lot of those conversations were difficult, and we asked a lot from the families during their crisis and from small hospitals at odd hours and often in unfamiliar realms of practice.

I also received the occasional odd request from families. I was asked to meet with a family "interested in organ donation." The patient had a significant stroke but was not brain dead, not close to brain dead, or even anticipated to progress to any form of death. But the family wanted the information, so I went to the hospital to meet with them, as part of our mandate was hospital and community education. It took a few minutes for me to figure out what the meeting was really about.

Out of the six family members I met with, there was only one interested in discussing organ donation. The other five were focused on long-term care, rehabilitation services, and the hope of recovery. They were appropriately skeptical as to why I was there, and at that point, I was too. The patient's cousin was the sixth family member and a long-term dialysis patient. He was interested in discussing the prospects of receiving his living cousin's kidney. It was a very awkward conversation in both the circumstances and the realization that the inquiring family member hadn't even taken the basic step of being evaluated for listing as a recipient. I redirected him and exited. There was enough distrust between the family and the medical community that I'm not sure when or if they realized who called for the meeting.

The toughest cases for me were often children or young adults. The most disturbing part was the randomness with which death often came: the two-year-old whose older sibling briefly left the pool gate open after school while their mom used the bathroom; the teacher who had parked her car to pick up the newspaper at the end of the driveway only to have the brakes fail, leaving her to be discovered under the vehicle by her husband; the Christmas Day gunshot wound to the head with the new job uniform plastic-wrapped in the trunk of the car; the medical student scheduled to start her first day on the transplant team arriving not as a student but as a victim of domestic violence; the many suicides and drug overdoses; a disturbing number of child shootings.

I had to learn and know each of these people so I could support their families in the crisis that transitioned to the act of organ donation. I felt I had a duty to connect and know them because anything less felt insincere.

The skills of actively listening, assimilating the information you've heard, and reflecting it back to families were among the assets of an organ transplant coordinator engrained in me. I also became acutely aware of my own limits and more comfortable with the task of asking others to engage with families when their expertise was critical. Evaluating a potential donor required a similar collaborative exchange to an effective palliative care consult. We periodically needed cardiology for echocardiograms, pulmonary for bronchoscopies, GI for scopes, nephrology, radiology, lab, pathology, the coroner, and always, neurology.

Katie

One of the more impactful cases reflecting the diversity of family and clinician interactions happened around the mid-point of my career as a transplant coordinator. I was called to a northern Pennsylvania hospital to evaluate a potential organ donor who had not yet been pronounced brain dead. Katie was a sixteen-year-old girl who'd arrived at the hospital as a trauma patient on a late spring afternoon.

Trauma can be both physical and psychological. Katie and five others suffered from the physical trauma. Everyone else connected to them or at the hospital dealt with the psychological trauma of the day.

Katie's parents were divorced and lived in separate states. She had an older brother, a younger sibling, and a stepmother. With the warmth of spring, it was a fun day to be out on a motorcycle. That week, Katie was visiting Pennsylvania to spend time with her father, Doug, and his wife, Arlene. He was enjoying the weather with his daughter on the back of his motorcycle. Arlene was also an avid motorcycle rider and out enjoying the day with them. When I arrived at the hospital, staff began debriefing and venting pieces of the narrative to me. They believed that perhaps Doug was making an effort to make up for the missed time in a separated family and wanted to excite and impress his daughter with a spirited ride.

Doug reportedly accelerated his motorcycle to about 150 miles per hour. The sound of the wind and the blur of the surroundings must've been an intoxicating experience. The region is mostly farm roads and a mix of hills, curves, and straight pieces of asphalt.

It was also a good day for four high school friends to be out together in a car. They might've seen the motorcycle coming and not calculated for the extreme speed. They were novice drivers and crossed the intersection, colliding wheel to side at roughly one hundred miles per hour.

Arlene heard the brakes and impact as she followed behind Katie and Doug. She arrived to a mind-altering trauma that even secondhand is difficult to recount. The impact had melded the motorcycle into the car frame. Most of the boys did not survive. Her husband was beyond the car with his helmet still on his head. The distance of the helmet from his shoulders told her all she needed to know about his status. She could go no closer to him. Katie? Katie was nowhere to be found.

The EMS crew arrived and began attending to the boys in the car. They spoke with Arlene and learned that she was distraught but physically okay. The search for Katie began anew. She wasn't in the car and not in view along the road. Some astute observer noted that the streetlight some twenty yards down the road was bent sideways with the light pole dangling oddly. The living boy was life-flighted out while a mix of EMS, fire, and police crew began to walk the brush beyond the light post. They found Katie there, breathing but not conscious.

I arrived at the hospital around twenty-four hours after the accident. It was a small enough community that most of the nurses, doctors, clerks, and respiratory therapists had a child or friend of a child who went to high school with the boys or knew their family. Some of the EMS and fire crew also worked at the hospital or were married to someone who did. People were a mix of angry, grieving, and hopeful. For some, there was even a sense of guilt in having so many conflicting emotions.

It was early enough in the day, and I was being kept updated on Katie's status as the morning progressed. Her mother, Jessica, drove overnight from South Carolina and on arrival, partnered up with Arlene in a sense of shared grief and foreboding. I stayed in the periphery and gathered what clinical information I could as the neurologic status began to be explored. Katie's first clinical exam was consistent with brain death. The trauma team began discussing the findings with the moms. I could see the quiet tears rolling down Jessica's face after the first family meeting.

The ICU team knew my role as a transplant coordinator. They did a good job at both keeping me up to date while conveying their desire to protect the moms from a perceived threat—the death that I represented. They knew organ donation would first mean a life had been lost, and Katie's was the one we were all in the middle of. Discussing that option with two grieving, exhausted, and traumatized women would mean facing that loss openly and then asking them for something.

The ICU team couldn't save Katie, and they struggled with how to serve and protect Jessica and Arlene from additional stress. Imagine how many directions a conversation with a woman who just lost her husband and stepdaughter, or ex-husband and daughter, could go.

As we waited for time to pass before the second brain death exam and apnea test, the ICU team drew screening labs and maintained Katie's blood pressure to preserve the option of donation. The pulmonologist asked if I needed anything from him before he went home to his high-school-age kids. I couldn't ethically ask for the bronchoscopy to assess for lung trauma, as the exam would incur some risk for the still clinically and legally alive Katie. She wasn't formally pronounced, so I told him I didn't need anything yet. He went home to his own grieving children.

The second brain-death exam was completed, and she lacked any signs of higher brain or brain stem function. The team prepared to sit down with the moms and discuss the information. I requested to join the meeting as a member of the team, assuring them that I'd observe the conversation and not discuss donation until after the apnea test. An arterial blood gas was being drawn to prepare for that step, and I was permitted to join the meeting.

The trauma team explained the neurologic findings of their clinical exam, efficiently presenting it with what felt like a balanced amount of clearly presented information. They reviewed that her brain swelling was visible on a CT scan and may have caused herniation compressing the brain stem. In a young person, there's less space for cerebral edema within the rigid confines of the skull.

There were deep breaths and tears as Jessica and Arlene heard the information. As they spoke, their insight became apparent.

Jessica said, "We know. I looked at Katie's eyes. She's not there anymore. I hate to ask this, but can she help anyone else…Can she donate her organs?"

In one sentence, I witnessed a previously fearful team switch from anxiety that I might open a difficult conversation to gratitude for my presence. I took the cue and introduced myself as the member of the team who could explore organ donation with them. I said we had some time to discuss that, but I wanted to know more about Katie first. I wanted to give them some space to introduce me to her as more than brain swelling, bruised ribs, fractured facial bones, and lost dreams.

Katie was an athlete on the lacrosse team and had a protective older brother, Justin. Even though she was described as a klutz and a straitlaced goofball by her close group of friends, she owned a skateboard. Due to her love of animals, she wanted to be a vet, yet she struggled with honors biology. She gave up some friends who explored drugs, and Justin had sternly and physically kept one "experimental" boy away earlier in the year.

I asked for permission to examine Katie. They joined me in the room until Katie's nurse asked them to step out as we repositioned and adjusted some things. I needed to conduct a neurologic exam. It wasn't my job to determine brain death, but I'd certainly stop a case if needed, and I still needed to look for indications that could potentially compromise donation.

I couldn't identify any brain stem or higher neurologic function. Her pupils were blown, the left side of her face bruised and swollen from impact. Her rib cage was also bruised. There were no tattoos, track marks, sores, scars, or evidence of STDs. From the right side of the bed, she looked like the healthy, athletic young lady they described. Ironically, it always bothered me to check the physical exam box "unremarkable" next to skin/visual exam. I felt guilty, like I should have something more to say about a person other than "unremarkable."

The ICU team completed an apnea test, and a time of death was pronounced. Jessica and Arlene understood this hours before the confirmatory exam and took the news quietly. At that point, they weren't just consenting for organ donation but yearning for some glimmer of positivity from deep tragedy. I sat back down with them and formally started the task of filling in the social history blanks and signing the papers consenting for organ and tissue donation.

I began, "What was her birthdate?"

"December 12 th."

"Did she smoke?"

"No."

"Drink alcohol?"

"No. She might've tried a beer, but otherwise, no."

"Any drugs?"

"Never."

"I didn't see any tattoos."

Both women laughed. "No."

"I hate to ask, but I have to. Any sexual history?"

There were some tears and a few sobs from both mothers.

Jessica, under her breath, whispered, "No."

It was as much an acknowledgment that that rite of passage was never to occur as it was an answer.

I paused before going on with more questions, but before I could resume, the door bounced open, and in came a man in jeans and a button-down shirt.

With a spirited voice, he said, "I'm Steve. I'm the coroner." He looked at me. "You're with Gift of Life, right?"

"Yes," I said. "I was just speaking with Katie's mom and stepmom." I motioned to the only other people in the room with the paper I was writing on, hoping to clue him in.

Steve failed to take the hint and responded, "Great! Can you share your information with me?"

That was something we routinely did, but I really wanted him to stop disrupting the conversation. His tone and focus were all wrong.

"Yes, of course."

To everyone's surprise, Steve again said, "Great!" He reached forward and took the papers right out of my hand before leaving the room. It wasn't remotely close to what I had in mind.

Arlene looked at me. "Can you make him go away?"

"I will gladly do everything I can," I told her.

For the next hour, I alternated between covering my questions and running coroner interference on the side.

Over the course of the evening, we completed the organ donation evaluation, and I was able to find recipients for Katie's kidneys, liver, and heart. At 11:00 p.m., I woke up the pulmonologist and asked him to come back to the hospital and perform a bronchoscopy.

He was supremely pissed and yelled, "You could've fucking done it at four!"

I was about to point out that she was legally alive then and circumstances had changed.

He blurted out, "No!" and hung up. He showed up fifteen minutes later and did the bronchoscopy. There was evidence of trauma, including bleeding and bruising in the lungs. We wouldn't be able to use them. I felt like shit for so many reasons.

The moms left sometime after midnight. They were entrusting me to carry their daughter's story and watch over her as she went to the OR. I took her to the OR sometime after three in the morning for a successful organ and tissue recovery.

I left the hospital around ten the morning after I arrived. They later informed me that the transplants went well, so I was able to send that information back to Jessica and Arlene. In addition, I helped research counselling services for Justin since he wasn't doing well with his sister's death. I don't imagine anyone was.

In the course of that experience, I'd gone from being perceived as a threat of difficult conversation to an ally and support system. The conversation the hospital team feared became the silver lining in a horrible storm. These became the skills I draw from in palliative care. I still wish Katie could've survived, and I imagine her as an adult, possibly with children of her own by now.

Burnout to Reinvention

The work life of transplant was brutal, but I did it as long as I could. After a few years of thirty-six-hour workdays, interstate travel, and deep sleep deprivation, I reached a breaking point and needed to scale back. I was having nightmarish dreams about work and was overly sensitized to every object that made a beeping noise. Even background sounds in music that might mimic a pager caused my heart rate to instantly rise. It wasn't long after I found myself sitting in scrubs on my back lawn with a cigar and a martini, dozing off at 10:00 a.m., that I actively looked for a transition. I hate cigars.

I took an easy job in Philadelphia at a law firm reviewing medical records and taking some transplant calls on weekends. It was easy money but only used a quarter of my brain power. I grew bored with consulting, so I checked out one of the hospitals I'd previously worked at and found an emergency room (ER) research position. Being in an ER could be perceived as a conflict of interest in transplant, so I alerted them to my coming resignation. I also signed up for a postgraduate family nurse practitioner program.

I did my last transplant case with a twenty-something girl whose complex elective brain surgery resulted in brain death. She had a benign mass compressing her optic nerve and blinding her. Before surgery, she told her family that if things went poorly, she wanted to be an organ donor. I fought hard to honor her wishes and closed my career with my one and only international organ procurement. I allocated her heart to a recipient in Canada due to matching challenges and an unfortunately timed fever in a local potential pediatric recipient. Life is fickle like that.

It was good to be back at my old hospital and even better to fearlessly sleep through the night, but it was months before I stopped waking with a start, wondering if I'd heard a non-existent pager.

A second round of grad school went well. Within a two-year time period, I had clinical rotations at A.I. DuPont, Planned Parenthood, an ENT practice, and the VA to name a few. I graduated and followed with some board prep courses and intensive study. I passed those and prepared for the next stage of my career as a nurse practitioner (NP). I married the wonderful woman who'd been through the past few years of this journey with me, and she finished her residency and gained a fellowship spot in Rochester, New York.

With her fellowship came a move to an area where I knew nobody. A lack of connection wasn't a great place to be as a freshly minted NP seeking employment, but I interviewed for a critical care position and a surgical position. The real break came when my neighbor, a senior partner at a competing practice, knocked on my door and asked if I was still looking for a job.

I joined Rochester Colorectal Surgeons and expanded into uncharted areas of practice for me. I took additional training and developed some operative skills while earning certification as a registered nurse first assistant. Robotic surgery is amazing in its capacity to facilitate things impossible for the human hand. On the clinical side, I was blessed with a skilled team who welcomed me into the family and taught me new skills.

One day a week, I observed with an HIV specialist who performed high-resolution anoscopy, looking for and treating anal dysplasia. A brief explanation would draw parallels between cervical pap smears and colposcopy to prevent cervical cancer. Because the human papilloma virus (HPV) is the cause of cervical and anal cancer and there are tissue similarities at the anal verge and cervix, the diagnostic and treatment options were similar.

I later grew a Friday specialty clinic to meet this need while spending other days in the OR, seeing consults, or in the office. Many of my patients were HIV positive or immunocompromised, as this presented a greater vulnerability to dysplasia. Others were young, surprised, and threatened. I served a diverse population of gay, straight, transgender, male, and female patients over my years there. It was interesting to see the number of patients sent with "hemorrhoids" that were really condyloma or genital warts. In one case, I found rectal adenocarcinoma, and we later went to the OR with other members of my team. It felt good to play a more direct role in saving a life. I developed the technical skills of doing ablations, biopsies, anoscopies, and injections while also de-escalating anxiety. To my surprise, I had one young man who held a full speaker-phone conversation while prone on the table mid-exam. There's certainly a diversity of humanity out there.

I left the colorectal surgery world after three years of practice. My wife had finished her fellowship, and we had two young girls. We looked back south to Pennsylvania where most of our family lived and had the fortune of finding job opportunities that matched our skills. My career in palliative medicine began there.

Palliative Care

I joined an established but growing palliative medicine consult service comprised of a multidisciplinary team from a variety of backgrounds and an outpatient team of six highly skilled nurse practitioners. When I started, the inpatient team consisted of three nurse practitioners and three doctors covering one hospital. I was able to complete and publish some research on the need for palliative care consult access in the rural community as a foundation for palliative telemedicine. We then covered two hospitals in person and, with some perseverance, launched a telemedicine practice covering a rural network hospital. Somehow, I earned a doctorate during that process.

The constantly changing inpatient team consisted of three doctors, two fellows, a social worker, a counselor, a chaplain, four nurse practitioners, a nurse, and administrative staff with a national presence in palliative care.

In a similar fashion to my transplant learning, we made a point of sharing the language we used and learning from the oncoming challenges we faced. We built partnerships with the teams we worked with regularly and grew to include an oncology palliative care clinic and further telemedicine outreach to regional hospitals. Palliative care is intensive in the world of relationship building and communication.

We have a team goal of equipping the larger healthcare network with some of the skills needed to engage in some primary palliative care. This is, in part, a motivating force behind this book. After all, many providers have long-standing relationships with their patients and should be prepared to have some difficult conversations with those who trust them.

CPR

The foundations of modern cardiopulmonary resuscitation (CPR) date back to the 1950s and 1960s, and research shows that the intervention of CPR saves approximately ninety-two thousand lives a year (Shaw, 2019).[24]

However, "saved" is a surprisingly nebulous term. For some, this is a raging success with a full return to functional living without residual effects of the cardiac arrest. The potential for this is greatest when we can fix, remove, or otherwise substantially address the cause. For many others is the return of a heartbeat and some level of cognitive injury from a lack of oxygen to the brain. Others may have a return of function only to face ongoing challenges or mortality in chronic or advanced illness. CPR doesn't fix organ failure, cure cancer, or reverse the natural entropy of aging.

There has been some research published regarding survival that is both surprising and worth considering. Krochmal et al. gathered five years of data, including 323 patients undergoing CPR. The good news was that over half survived. Of the study group, 59.4 percent had a return of spontaneous circulation (ROSC), meaning the heart was restarted. Great! But before we get tachycardic with excitement, we should consider only 13 percent survived to be discharged from

---

[24] Elizabeth Shaw, "The History of CPR," ProCPR, last modified April 10, 2019, https://www.procpr.org/blog/misc/history-of-cpr

that hospital stay. Even less—only 2.9 percent—survived if CPR needed to be repeated.[25]

Clearly, CPR is not the panacea that's presented in the movies.

Millions of people, both clinical and lay person, have received instructions in both CPR and first aid. The foundations for modern CPR originated as far back as the 1700s, while the modern approach was only established in the past century. The French Academy of Sciences recommended mouth-to-mouth resuscitation for drowning victims in 1740 (Shaw, 2019).[26] Dr. Friedrich Mass's first documented attempts at chest compressions came over a hundred years later in 1891. In 1903, a breakthrough occurred with the first documented successful intervention with chest compressions. W. B. Kouwenhoven, J. R. Jude, and G. G. Knickerbocker first published on the potential for closed cardiac massage in the 1960s.[27] That work became the foundation for modern CPR and later became incorporated with pioneering research in defibrillation and the electrophysiology of the heart. We now have internal and external defibrillators, with the latter being fairly ubiquitous in public spaces; portable face masks for rescue breathing; and Ambu bags for manual "breath giving." Mechanized devices, such as the Lucas device, can give compressions without use of hand contact. Entire invasive cardiology programs have grown up to provide emergency catheter lab intervention for a myocardial infarction or cardiac arrest. There are formal classes, books, pamphlets, YouTube videos, and songs identified for compression pacing, such as "Stayin' Alive" by the Bee Gees, along with countless dramatic representations of CPR in

---

[25] Rebecca L. Krochmal et al., "Family Presence at First Cardiopulmonary Resuscitation and Subsequent Limitations on Care in the Medical Intensive Care Unit," *American Journal of Critical Care* 26, no. 3 (2017): 221-228, https://doi.org/10.4037/ajcc2017510

[26] Shaw, "This History of CPR."

[27] W. B. Kouwenhoven, J R Jude, and G G Knickerbocker, "CLOSED-CHEST CARDIAC MASSAGE," *JAMA* 173, no. 10 (September 1960): 1064-1067, https://doi.org/10.1001/jama.1960.03020280004002

medical, action, and comedy films, as well as TV and social media vignettes. Some of these media representations are purely for entertainment and parody the real intensity of CPR. Other portrayals are entertainment in intent but fall into the realm of believable for the uninformed. I try not to scream at the TV when I see a "patient" talking with an endotracheal tube in place.

In most ways, we're light-years away from what we could do at the point of death in past decades. Ventilators and the growing utilization of venous-to-venous and venous-to-arterial ECMO circuits come to mind. But in other ways, we've made little substantial movement from bloodletting, leaches, and blowing smoke up your ass in terms of our decision-making and social understanding of CPR, its merits, detriments, and implications. Some who read that sentence may be jolted at seeing the phrase "blowing smoke up your ass." The phrase is a euphemism for a lie or falsehood, but while it may have become a euphemism, it was also once considered a legitimate treatment for drowning.[28] How things have changed.

Social media references and images of CPR are easy to find; however, a rational dialogue about the intervention and informed decision-making around its appropriate application is less common and virtually absent in the realm of entertainment. Humanity, in my experience, has a love affair with the outliers. Most of us reading this text can think of cases from our own social networks or clinical experience. The patient who beat the odds and defied anticipation is far more appealing and memorable than the median experience. Hope is a survival mechanism and sometimes lives with the outliers. It is, after all, those who live who get to tell their story while the majority become silent. Fully informed conversations about the option of CPR are about exploring whether the reality of it has the potential to offer you what you hope for or things worse than blowing smoke.

It's not uncommon to encounter patients with end-stage medical conditions and advanced age who are labeled as "full code" in the

---

[28] All That's Interesting, "When 'Blowing Smoke Up Your Ass' Was Much More Than Just A Saying," All That's Interesting, last modified March 6, 2020, https://allthatsinteresting.com/blowing-smoke-up-your-ass

electronic medical record. But many of these same patients also have advanced directives indicating that they don't desire chest compressions, breathing tubes, feeding tubes, or dialysis at the end of life. The uncomfortable gray zone lies in the variability with which individuals define words such as "terminal" or "end of life." Is end of life the day we're dying? The week? The month? Or the year? Does the likelihood of returning to an acceptable quality of life factor into the decision? How does the present quality of life influence the conversation? Your perception of quality of life and what you're willing to undergo may vary wildly from my perceptions. So often I encounter patients who are full code because the manner in which the code status question was posed is completely uninformed. The potentially detailed and complex question of the pros and cons is often narrowed to seven words: "Do you want us to do everything?"

CPR has its greatest value when there's something we can fix after the fact and provides a baseline quality of life acceptable to the patient. This is more apparent in the patient with an acute myocardial infarction (MI), the drowning patient, or the drug overdose, to name a few. We can address the coronary artery disease in the cardiac cath lab or operating room. We have the ability to restore breathing, reverse a toxin, or engage the addicted in rehab. The outcome of both CPR and ongoing medical management is always uncertain, but if there's ultimately nothing we can fix, treat, cure, or effectively manage, then CPR has a reduced value as a medical intervention. For example, the medical utility of CPR is less apparent in the elderly patient with multiple health problems such as end stage heart disease, advanced cancer, COPD, and dementia. At no point do these more objective observations regarding medical utility have any relationship to the value of that human being. The Nobel laureate or the brother with a heroin addiction are both loved by their families and will address mortality from their own standpoints. Their quality of life and the implications of CPR as it relates to their active health concerns remain the objective elements in the discussion. I'd caution you to view quality of life from the patient's perspective and not your own. I've encountered many patients with a quality of life most would find untenable, yet they prove capable of expressing contentment, joy, and rich engagement. Their quality is good. What does CPR offer them in their physical state?

As a palliative care provider, it's ethically important for me to recognize that people have the right to make decisions differing from the ones I'd make for myself or my loved ones. Changing someone's mind on the topic of code status is never my job. Rather, it's my role and ethical duty to engage the sometimes difficult exploration of what a full code status would or wouldn't offer a person as it relates to the values they're willing to share with me. If a patient can accurately conceptualize their health status and share a rationale for a choice, I'll endeavor to express it to the team so that it's honored, even if I disagree.

As we consider factors influencing healthcare decision-making, we must understand that our perception of quality of life is not a universal experience. For example, a thirty-eight-year-old man who suffered a spinal injury and became quadriplegic in his teens may still live a rich and engaging life and view that quality to be more than adequate. A seventy-eight-year-old with new hemiplegia from a stroke may also have a completely different opinion at the time of the stroke or in the following months. Perception of quality of life is personal and variable, and I have no right to blindly prescribe my own values.

When I engage a conversation about code status, it's typically after I've assessed the patient's understanding of their health and taken the time to fill in some of the knowledge gaps. This might not be in possible in an emergency, in the middle of the night, or if the patient lacks capacity.

If I do have a patient with capacity or a healthcare agent, I often say, "Tell me what you're hearing about your health status."

The answers which might follow this broad question can be informing and surprising. I've had patients who were actively receiving chemotherapy for two months who didn't understand they had cancer.

"No, they said I have carcinomatosis in my belly," is one response I recall.

I'm going to model a conversation and, to the extent that text will allow, use the language that I often do in the dialogue. Feel free to take what you desire and restructure what you wish. You may observe that as I begin to form a rapport with the patient and family, the code status questions are at the tail end of the conversation. This may vary depending on the present urgency, but if I'm doing it right, I need to know who my patient is beyond a collection of diagnosis.

I'd begin with, "Hello, Mildred. My name is Craig, and I'm part of the palliative care team here at the hospital. I've been asked to meet with you and your family to support you as you deal with complex health concerns in an effort to better navigate healthcare decisions. We want to make sure we handle things the way you'd like us to. I've spent some time reviewing your medical records, and we can discuss that in a bit. First, tell me, how are you doing right now?"

This entry allows the beginning of a rapport and a typically non-threatening review of symptoms. I'm learning about the patient and family with these questions, and I hope they see that I'm invested in their story. They should trust me less if I'm not. She and the family are assessing me as much as I'm learning about her present status. When the family is present, I also want to hear their impressions of how she's doing. Sometimes, naming things creates a different level of consciousness about what they're observing. I may reflect back what they're saying and name my own observations. Being validated and noticed shows attentiveness and concern, and if there are significantly acute worries, these may need to be addressed first. A pain crisis may be the only relevant topic in the moment. Barring that, I'm going to want to elicit more about the quality of life prior to that day.

Next, I'd ask, "Tell me how you were doing last week? How were you last month? When did things begin to change? When did you last feel well?"

Clinically, I do want to know what's changed, but I also want them to name this out loud in their own voice and in the company of family. The patient might've been doing great up until last week or name a deep sense of loss and difficulty lasting years. On more than one occasion, I've been asked to see a patient, and the answers revealed a missed diagnosis or a significant insight. For example, one exchange revealed a patient not with terminal dementia needing hospice as the consult ordered requested, but a fully functional member of society with a urinary tract infection and associated encephalopathy.

I'd continue and ask, "Take me way back—ten, twenty, thirty years. What did you do for a living? What did you do for fun?"

Usually, people or family can easily rattle off what they did for a living. Some of the careers fascinate me or connect us.

"Oh, you're a teacher. I come from a family of teachers. Where did you teach?"

Other answers speak to the hardships of life as well as the joys. People will usually chuckle when I re-ask the question, "What did you do for fun?"

The majority of patients don't volunteer the answer to that question the first time. If they do begin to answer, the more complete story of who they are and their identity really emerges. This matters for a multitude of reasons: I'm learning about their education level, their family structure, how they value their time, and what's important to them. When the patient and family know I see them for who they are, then I really can do a better job advocating for them from a position of understanding. I need to see them as an individual human being.

Some other reasons why these questions are valuable are less obvious. Later in the conversation, I'm likely to ask a few questions that can be difficult to both hear and answer. In some ways, this conversation is a bit like a delicate dance.

Imagine you are the patient for a moment. I'll tell you where I'm going to place my feet in this dance and then step there. I may need a comfortable place for both of us to step back. If I know enough about you, I may be trusted to take that step and also know where we can step back to if we need a moment.

Next, I'd say, "I know you've been going through a great deal these past weeks/months/years medically. Can you tell me what puts a smile on your face lately? What brings you joy?"

This question helps me understand how they're coping and may allow a more honest representation of their perception of their quality of life. The answer is often family. Ironically, that answer is often the same for a later question.

In a difficult consult, I get one-word answers, a flat or hostile demeanor, and closed doors to dialogue. In a bit of therapeutic dark humor in a team meeting, I coined the term "psychosocial asystole" to describe that challenge. If things are going well, I have a good start in understanding who the patient and family are. I'm not done learning, but I need to shift gears to assess their knowledge of the medical condition. Here are some of the questions that help me understand this.

I'd move on to, "What brought you to the hospital? Or, tell me what you're hearing from the medical team about how you're doing and what your biggest medical concerns are."

As the patient and family answer, it helps me see the critically important gaps in medical understanding. I reflect back what's accurate and begin to fill in what's missing. Because I'm also the new guy in the room and despite the depth of the medical record, it's not uncommon for the family to fill in my own gaps in understanding. I'll be upfront about the limits of my knowledge, as well as other pending diagnostic testing and consults that might help inform everyone.

I'm also getting a feel for how the patient and family like their information. Some folks like a very basic unpolished overview of the big picture—"Don't sugar coat it, just tell it to me straight." Others want detailed minutia and might struggle to see past finite data points to the big picture. Some have the whole picture and "get it." Most are in between, and each family member may be at a different point of comprehension. The challenge of a good consult is trying to bring everyone to the common ground of understanding when you might begin with a torrent of information bursting from a fire hose.

One question comes with a warning: "The next question I'm going to ask may be easy, or it may be deceptively difficult. It's intentionally broad—tell me what you're worried about the most."

If I'm trying to clarify goals of care and get to a code status conversation, this question is critical. If the conversation gets dark and difficult, I hopefully know the person well enough to understand when and where to periodically retreat. The most common answer is again "family," often followed by "dying." The answers are often completely surprising and may only be loosely related to the medical concerns.

Contrast the implications of these two answers: "I had a good life. I'm not worried about much" versus "I'm worried about my nephew and his kids. He's disabled, and his three kids live with us. His wife is dead, and Mikey, the middle kid, has autism. They live with me and depend on my social security check to make rent. I can't die!"

Worry about leaving family behind as well as missing major life events may inform the rationale behind the healthcare decisions they make.

"I'm worried about missing my son's wedding." The follow-up conversation will be different if there's a fiancée and a date versus learning the son is in second grade. I've had both answers, and I've also attended a few hospital wedding ceremonies.

You may notice that the questions above have the potential to build decent rapport and sizeable amounts of information regarding the gestalt of the patient's values long before I raised the topic of code status. There's not always time for this, but I hope to convey the difference between an informed discussion leading to code status instead of just asking the seven words, "Do you want us to do everything?"

"I'm going to ask some questions that may be difficult to hear and difficult to answer. I ask them now because it's important to talk about these things while we can and not in an emergency, but I'm not asking because I expect anything to happen. Do you have a living will?" Regardless of whether the answer is yes or no, it still needs real time interpretation.

I'd then say, "I'm going to ask the questions that are typically on a living will in a hypothetical manner and in the context of your healthcare challenges. If you were here, or at home, or at another place, and someone walked in to check on you and found that you didn't have a heartbeat and had died, we have two choices to make in that moment. One choice is to say that your death is unfortunate but natural and leave you in peace. The other choice is to be medically aggressive. This would include CPR, where we compress the chest to squeeze blood out into circulation. In someone my age—forties—this is very physical and will separate cartilage and break ribs. What it won't do is fix your underlying health problems."

If relevant, I name the problems or use different language if something is fixable.

"I want to be clear. I'm not talking about stopping any medical treatment. We keep doing what we're doing. This is a conversation about what we do when those things fail. How do you want us to respond when we encounter death? Leave you in peace or do CPR?"

Often, the patient or family I'm speaking with give me a very clear answer before I use all of the language described above. Sometimes, I need to affirm their decision or clarify further: "I hear what you're saying is…" If there's an answer, I repeat it back and tell them what I'll be doing with that information. Even if the answer is specific, I may give the data point on thirty-day survival either to affirm a choice or allow the patient or family the full information so they can evaluate. It's okay if the group is unable to make a decision. There are times when we're waiting for diagnostic results to come back, the counsel of a specialty, the presence of a family member, or just need time to absorb it all. If it's a critically time sensitive conversation, I'll point out to the family that in the absence of a decision, we'll perform CPR in the event of death and alert them after.

Some patients answer this question easily, but it's a shock for others. They can defer to a family member, and we can form a plan to think on it and revisit. In the majority of the discussions, there's a sense of relief that someone's asked this, and we move on. Some conversations are relatively easy while others don't seem to go very well. I have the great fortune of typically having a colleague join me for many of these. Both the counselor and social worker on my team have great skills at reframing language, catching additional questions, and following up after I've left. This is the beauty of a team.

While ventilators are and should be linked to the CPR conversation, I have separated this a bit in the way I've presented the conversation above. I usually address intubation and ventilator use as the second question in the code status dialogue. It should also serve as a clue that there's a knowledge deficit if the patient says, "I never want a breathing tube, but you can do CPR." A side conversation discussing the "P" for "pulmonary" in CPR should follow.

When exploring a patient's wishes surrounding intubation and ventilation, I start by stating some pertinent interventions that can be engaged to prevent respiratory failure. The obligation to facilitate an informed decision is the same.

"If you start to have difficulty breathing, we can turn up your oxygen, give you a diuretic, add a bronchodilator, even switch to Optiflow^tm or BiPAP support in hopes of improving your breathing. If those things fail, should we ever insert a tube and have a ventilator—a machine—breathe for you?" There can be additional interventions, and what is relevant should be included.

Just like with the CPR questions, some individuals will have a ready answer, and others will have a knowledge gap or further relevant questions. I might point out that sometimes the use of a ventilator can be a temporary event while the team works to eliminate the need for this support and make sure that the risks and alternatives to its use are understood as well.

I explain, "For some people with end-stage lung disease or advanced lung cancer, there's a risk that we may not be able to get them off a breathing machine. If breathing fails, the alternative to the machine is focusing on your comfort and preventing respiratory failure from feeling distressful. This means death is likely to follow."

If a patient answers that they'd be willing to accept the use of a ventilator, then we need to explore further to find out if there's an endpoint.

"While you're on a breathing machine, you won't be able to speak, and food will be provided via a temporary tube. If we're unable to get you off the machine, should we ever make it permanent or semi-permanent? We do this through surgical placement of a tracheostomy and care in a specialized nursing home."

I should be clear that as I engage the framework of the language above, I'm seated, speaking slowly and clearly, and reading the body language of the family. Emotions will be present, and silence may be uncomfortable. The framework is tailored a bit differently for each family rapport and set of circumstances. With repeated discussions, there are some generalizable similarities once you develop an informative approach to discussing this sometimes sensitive yet important topic. What follows are a few atypical examples.

Caroline

Caroline was eighty-six, and her husband, Edward, appeared a bit older. They consulted me to clarify goals of care while Caroline was in our ICU, admitted with a malignant pleural effusion from her metastatic lung cancer. I stepped into the room behind patient transport to see her struggling to breathe, even with the support of a BiPAP mask. She was being picked up for interventional radiology for an urgently needed thoracentesis and likely PleurX™ drain placement to remove fluid from around the lung. She'd been admitted for the same concern about a week earlier, and clearly, the fluid would re-accumulate again. I gave a very brief greeting and told her I'd see her when she returned.

Caroline had been a smoker most of her life, and the pressure of gravity and time conspired to collapse portions of her spine. Her kyphosis made the combination of COPD and lung cancer a considerable and present threat. Despite that, she was actively receiving immunotherapy in the months preceding that most recent string of hospital admissions.

When Caroline returned to the room, she appeared quite different than the elderly woman in duress who'd rolled by me a few hours earlier. She breathed considerably better and with only the aid of nasal cannula oxygen, and the absence of the BiPAP mask made communication much easier. Edward had also arrived and sat in a chair against the wall at the foot of the bed, his cane resting next to him. I reintroduced myself, and we got to the work of knowing each other and exploring the goals of care.

Caroline was a retired educator who had served in a gritty community in North Philadelphia. Edward was her caretaker in her journey with cancer. They'd been married some fifty years and had two older daughters. One was estranged while the other, Madeline, was involved but lived in Boston. The apple didn't fall too far from the tree as they told me she was a social worker for children and youth. Edward mentioned that he'd been abstaining from surgical intervention for his own cancer. He didn't want to be unavailable for Caroline. These were people who were accustomed to adversity throughout their lives.

Caroline's tenacity shone through in most of our conversation. The goals were to accept further immunotherapy as long as it was being offered, and she was able to independently state that her cancer was terminal. She reflected back on her life and the shared experiences with Ed as being a success. She could accept that her life would end but was in no rush to get there, and they'd not taken the time to complete an advanced directive.

When we got to the point of discussing code status, Caroline grew quiet and Ed spoke up. We'd talked about her advanced cancer, her frail bones, and what CPR and breathing tubes could and couldn't fix.

"Tell the man what you want. We talked about this."

Caroline spoke about her mother's death many years before in an ICU on a ventilator. "I don't want to go like that. When my time comes, I'd rather go peacefully, without tubes." Then the real concern was voiced. "But I'm afraid of what my daughter will say. She'll be furious!"

I offered to call and have the same conversation with Madeline.

"Madeline doesn't want to lose her mommy." The way she said it came as a bit of a warning.

Ed leaned forward, clasping his cane, and spoke to his wife again, saying, "This is about what *you* want."

I restated that the general plan was full medical support, short of CPR and intubation. My next step was to follow through on my commitment to call Madeline and discuss her "mommy's" wishes. With Caroline's blessing, I entered the change in code status into the computer. It was two in the afternoon, and I left the room to find a quiet place to call Madeline. There was only one number listed in the records, and it proved to be a work cell phone.

I left her my name and two contact numbers and included my title and role as a palliative care provider in clarifying her mom's goals of care. I didn't receive a call back at either of the numbers I had provided.

I felt like things had been left unresolved as I signed my consult note at the end of the day. I finished my rounds and recorded a sign out for the team. The next day was a needed day off.

I took my pager home with me, recognizing that since I held the conversation with them earlier, I might be the only one to be best prepared to continue it. I spent that particular day helping a friend with some manual labor, returning the page from Caroline's team when I returned home in the afternoon. Madeline had been by to see her mother and was angered by the change in code status. She leveraged her influence as the only involved child, and her mom relented, so the team changed it back. She wanted to speak with me.

The next day, I followed up with Caroline and was pleased to see that she looked about as good as she could with multiple advanced illnesses. She'd graduated from the ICU and was seated in a bedside chair with nasal cannula oxygen. She had more of the gritty spunk to her personality that I'd glimpsed earlier, her only complaint being some chest pressure where the PleurX[tm] drain had been placed. We chatted for a bit before we revisited her code status. She confirmed that she didn't wish to receive CPR or ventilator support at the end of life. The more important part for her was not the threat of unwanted heroics but the threat of failing her daughter. We talked about that for a while. She had capacity, and her priority was to honor her daughter's wishes over her own. Based on that desire, I left her code status as full code.

Later that afternoon, I followed up and returned Madeline's call. She was back at work, and a distinct frostiness coated the opening to our conversation. I described my role in learning a patient's values and priorities so we could best match them to available care options. We discussed her tenacity and humor as much as her marching frailty, and for a while the conversation was cordial. I then asked her to help me understand how her mother's code status changed.

"I didn't think it was the right thing. My mother wants to live."

"I have little doubt about that. Believe me, I definitely want her to live." I liked the spunky kyphotic woman with the robust personality. "I just want you to know, though, that CPR and intubation do have a poor prospect of offering life in the setting of progressive metastatic lung cancer, advanced COPD, and restrictive lung disease from kyphosis."

"I understand," she said. "I'll make a decision when the time comes."

For better or worse, death didn't always come with warning or any semblance of an appointment. An emergency was a poor time to make a decision, and phone calls often came after a CPR event.

I took the risk of sharing that her mother had expressed her wishes to me in tandem with the fear that her daughter would be angry. It was perhaps not the best thing to say, as it only further entrenched her personal point of view and limited any further constructive dialogue. I worried that Caroline would receive interventions selected in deference to her daughter when it was too late for her to discuss it with her. Death rarely has a predictable schedule, after all. I was concerned for her frail but stately spouse as well.

Madeline asked what her mother's code status was, so I shared that it was full code, and I had no intention of changing it. It was my job to support Caroline's informed decision, even if I was uncomfortable with how she arrived at it.

Pauline

During some consults, you make your introduction, assess the patient's knowledge, and find glaring cavities in their understanding. Other times, the patient requests your consultation and makes it abundantly clear that they have a full grasp of their mortality and exactly how they want it handled.

Pauline, then in her seventies, and her late husband had been life-long smokers. When she wasn't working next to him rebuilding muscle car engines, she worked as a waitress in the decades where smoking was the norm in many establishments. She even remembered smoking in her hospital room when a few of her children were born—three of them following in her footsteps. Decades of first and second-hand smoking had contributed to debilitating COPD, the same disease that killed her husband, Marty.

This was her fourth or fifth hospitalization in the past year from her end-stage lung disease. We spoke about her lung disease and the changes that came with navigating each step with an oxygen tank in tow. She admitted that she wasn't recovering after each hospitalization, and catching her breath was harder to come by. We discussed this as her baseline reserve. Her ability to bounce back, due to the consistent presence of the disease, was not as robust as before.

She reflected that her life had moved on from her days of muscle cars and illegal drag races. I wasn't telling her any of this; she was telling me. Then she shared with me why she asked for a palliative care consultation.

"I don't want my last days to be stuck on a damn machine. I love my family, but I'm afraid of what they'll do." Her family was her biggest source of joy at that stage. As the matriarch of an energetic bunch of people, her pleasure often came from just listening to the noise of family swarming around her. Six kids resulted in a whopping sixteen grandkids. The subtle tint of fluorescent purple in her hair was the outcome of time with one granddaughter. She started naming them before her dyspnea broke the stream. We paused the dialogue for a physical assessment—more to let her catch her breath.

In the course of an hour, we clarified her wishes for code status, and I committed to documenting them in the electronic medical record. I took the time to hear her concerns and validate them. I suggested we pull together her children and spend a bit of time discussing what her advanced care planning wishes were, and she agreed. With that, I made a call to her eldest daughter and set up a family meeting for the next day at eleven.

I arrived at her room around 10:45 a.m. to get a bit of an update on her status before the meeting. She spotted me in the doorway and waved me in. Four of her children and three teen to young adult grandkids were already there.

Pauline sat in a chair at the foot of her bed while her family took up perches on the bed, counter, and against the window. I navigated over the oxygen tubing and took up my favored seat on top of the trash can lid, eye level to everyone in the room. I began to introduce myself before pausing as cell phones came out to reach other family members on speakerphone.

"My name is Craig, and I'm part of a palliative medicine service. My role is to work with patients and families dealing with complex illness to address symptoms or navigate decision-making. We're having this meeting today to explore what some of her priorities are so we do a better job of providing care to her the way she wants us to and avoid doing things she doesn't want." I shared that I'd met with Pauline yesterday and spent some time talking with her.

"Can you tell me what you're hearing from the medical team about how your mom is doing?"

Gradually, family members began to speak up.

Her son said, "She's doing fine at home."

"No, she isn't," one daughter said. "I mean, okay, but she has been in the hospital three times this fall."

"She's been having a rough time, but she's a fighter," her other daughter replied.

"I think she's strong, but she has a hard time getting out of the house and into the car. Things aren't great," her granddaughter added.

I took this as a moment to give a recap of the hospital course. "It looks like she came in with pneumonia on top of her advanced COPD. She seems to have responded to a course of some steroids, inhalers, and antibiotics. Her x-ray will never be normal, but it's a bit better, and the amount of oxygen she needs has reduced. We appear to be turning the corner from a near crisis." I pointed out that she was very close to needing ICU care two days ago.

Many people don't comprehend COPD as a slowly progressive terminal condition. The curve has a great deal of variability influenced by lung damage, general health, and engagement with treatment. I pointed out that Pauline had been doing most things right and validated that it was evidence of her being a "fighter."

"When most people have a flair up of a disease, it chips away at their reserve. She's had a lot of flair ups in a short amount of time, and I think her reserve, the ability to bounce back, is being reduced."

They nodded in acknowledgment, then I began to bridge the conversation to advanced care planning.

I motioned to Pauline. "We talked yesterday, and I asked some questions. One of those was what was most important to her. She mentioned all of you, and I think one of you might be why her hair is purple." There were some turned heads and an audible chuckle on the speaker phone. "Your mom also told me she wants to keep up with treatment and oxygen and come back to the hospital if she needs to, and we can and will support that. Then we moved on to some difficult stuff. We know one of these days that treatment will fail, and we discussed how she wants that handled.

"We talked about the questions that are typically on a living will, wanting to have the discussion while we weren't in the middle of an emergency. When encountering death, we have a choice: allow it to be something natural, or engage in some aggressive medical interventions.

"CPR is very physical and can do some damage, but it won't resolve her COPD."

Pauline interjected, "I don't want that!"

The room was quiet for a few beats.

Over the speaker phone, we could hear her child say through tears, "Okay, Mom."

"If her breathing is struggling, we can do what we've done now—add more oxygen and different supports like Optiflow™ or BiPAP in the ICU. If those things fail, she doesn't want a breathing tube. Sometimes, we can use them temporarily and get them back out, but there's always a risk with end-stage COPD that we can't, and she doesn't want us to go that far. We've documented that in our computer, but I thought it was more important for all of you to know."

"I don't want a tube down my throat. If I'm that bad, make it so I don't suffer, and then cremate me," Pauline said.

To my surprise, a bit of an argument broke out, but it wasn't at all about code status. Everyone seemed to have quickly accepted her statements on that. Their argument centered around insisting that she be buried and not cremated. They even moved past that point of contention without her and started debating where she'd be buried.

With that, the purple-haired, muscle-car-building matriarch of the family raised her voice a notch. She looked at me but seemed to know they'd stop talking and listen.

"And when I die!" She paused for a breath. "And when I am cremated!" Another pause. "They can take my ashes…and they can put them in an etch-a-sketch and play with my knobs all day long!" The room roared with laughter.

We adjourned the meeting.

Quinton

Code status conversations are a normal part of almost every palliative care consultation. The difficult ones come through language barriers, families who push their wishes above the patient, or the abrupt onset of an emergency. Sometimes, a sense of urgency is less evident through the distance of a phone but obvious in person.

This last story takes place in a medical ICU.

Quinton was forty-seven and struggled with a lifetime of depression and methodical, unrelenting alcohol abuse culminating in liver failure. He'd declined the option of an organ transplant, as he didn't wish to stop drinking. He came to our ICU with liver failure, hepato-renal failure, and massive anasarca. He was encephalopathic and working hard to breathe. One of the first things we did was calculate his MELD score—the calculation of liver function ranging from six to forty with transplant consideration presenting around eighteen.[29]

His MELD score was nearly forty, and he was actively drinking days before this admission. His projected survival from his liver numbers alone was near 10 percent over the next ninety days.

---

[29] "Transplant Medicine: MELD Score and 90-Day Mortality Rate for Alcoholic Hepatitis," Mayo Clinic, Mayo Foundation for Medical Education and Research, accessed June 5, 2021, https://www.mayoclinic.org/medical-professionals/transplant-medicine/calculators/meld-score-and-90-day-mortality-rate-for-alcoholic-hepatitis/itt-20434719

I often said I didn't have a crystal ball when giving a range for prognosis, but his multisystem organ failure made his immediate critical care future look closer to futile. The ICU team formed this opinion as well and asked for help in clarifying his goals of care.

Quinton's parents were an educated elderly couple who gave the impression of being beaten down while caring for their son. They sat in chairs at the foot of the bed, and our conversation moved quickly as I gathered some social history. He'd been drinking pretty heavily for the better part of thirty years, even trying rehab three times at his parents begging, but hadn't managed to stay sober for more than the odd month. He'd worked the occasional job, but the alcohol always got in the way. His parents continued to support him during most of those years with food and a roof over his head.

I was sitting with my back to Quinton and started to broach the topic of code status. ICU nurses rarely mince their words, and Quinton's tapped me on the shoulder and said, "We need to make a decision now!"

His dad heard and looked at me, stating, "He's been trying to kill himself for years with this."

I turned to face Quinton and saw his oxygen numbers were down, his effort to breathe up, and a small mass of anxious residents and the attending physician standing at the doorway.

Looking back at his mom and dad, I could see they loved him deeply. They'd cared for him as best they could despite his disease for most of their lives.

"We could put a breathing tube in and support him, but his prognosis won't really change."

"Is he dying?" his mom asked.

"Yes."

"He'd be angry if we forced things on him."

"We can allow him to die without a breathing tube and try to make him comfortable."

"That's what he'd want," his dad said, tears in his eyes.

Quinton's nurse had been standing there, waiting for an answer. With the dad's words, she calmly turned and walked to the doorway crowd, stating, "Comfort."

Futility is often a sticky thing to determine. The team that day was in full agreement. By the narrowest of margins, we avoided prolonging Quinton's death by multiple days, tests, procedures, and interventions—a death that could arguably have been uncomfortable for the patient and traumatic for those who loved him.

Far less important to every palliative care provider is the secondary reality that we probably spared the healthcare system the expense of hundreds of thousands of dollars that wouldn't have led to a different outcome.

For the remainder of the afternoon, we cared for him and for his parents as well. He died about three hours later.

Artificial Nutrition

As I'm writing this, it's the day before Thanksgiving in 2019. I'm developing plans for multiple family gatherings over food in the back of my mind. There will be turkey, stuffing, potatoes, cranberry, and a variety of sides organized by my mother-in-law at my house. After dinner, some of us will leave the table and drive across town to join other family at my brother's house for the dinner he and his girlfriend are hosting. We mostly plan on a dessert feast there.

Food often has deep meaning, though that varies based on personal and cultural aspects. If we think about most family gatherings, food is often a central point. The specifics may change between holidays, weddings, funerals, baby showers, birthday parties, christenings, and bar/bat mitzvahs, but the social connection is the same. On a deep level, we have a tendency to provide sustenance as an expression of love and caring. It's more than just essential to life—it's deeply intertwined in our interpersonal connectedness. Because of this, conversations surrounding artificial feeding, anorexia, cachexia, dysphagia, nutrition, and pleasure are often layered with factors influencing decision-making.

When I meet with families to explore goals of care, the consult request often identifies artificial nutrition as the central question needing clarification. The family meeting starts out with the same steps of identifying the key decision-makers, including the patient, followed by an assessment of their understanding of their health problems. What do they know, and how do they know it? Has there been a family experience with artificial nutrition that's similar or widely divergent from the story at hand? As a clinician, I also have to explore whether or not there are alternatives.

Ironically, the most common alternative is having the patience to allow for a period of recovery. On multiple occasions, I've been asked to meet with a stable but encephalopathic patient who's been unable to pass a swallowing evaluation. The patient may be stable enough to leave the tertiary care center for short-term rehab, but in the medicolegal world, not well enough to eat safely. This is an unfortunate phenomenon that results from the pressure to move patients as part of the healthcare business. It could be that "the patient has been here too long and is stable," "The skilled nursing facility (SNF) won't take them if they're not eating," or "The SNF won't take the patient with a temporary feeding tube such as a Dobhoff." This is amplified during the maturing flu season by concerns about bed availability.

A quick generic example might be the seventy-eight-year-old woman who comes in with confusion and stroke-like symptoms. As we go through the workup, we determine that this isn't an acute CVA and not end-stage dementia but something as simple as urosepsis. We clear the infection, but the encephalopathy, lethargy, and refusal to attend to food become a time-sensitive problem. If this patient was a fully functional member of society prior to hospitalization, there's a good likelihood that her mind will clear the toxicity of infection and she'll be able to eat again. This may take days, or it may take weeks. These are the families where I recommend that we push back against the pressures of the system and consider a temporary feeding tube. We can raise code status and the question of long-term feeding tube placement without finalizing an answer to the latter part of the question: time. Time is often the first answer. For some, it allows the body to restore the ability to swallow.

However, for other patients, time has been the enemy that leads us to conversations about the pros and cons for artificial feeding options. There are two questions worth considering with the patient and family. Does the option of artificial feeding afford us time to complete treatment and recovery from the present health problem? This may mean recovery from things such as head and neck cancer or time to rehabilitate from a stroke. Does artificial feeding offer us time to enjoy more of an acceptable quality of life or experience unrelenting suffering? The insidious march of dementia is an example of where time has progressed with an irreversible state of decline but may or may not be perceived as suffering or meaningless.

The procedure of placing a PEG tube is often not that complicated. Early in my career when I worked in critical care, patients in need of a PEG tube would have it placed at bedside, and we'd begin using it the next day, with few patients needing surgical placement. It's perhaps this procedural ease that resulted in a clinical culture where we offered and placed them readily in the past. This is gradually changing as a few of my gastroenterologist colleagues question the ethics and merits in some cases and periodically refuse to passively play along.

Phillip

Phillip was a long-haul truck driver who weighed in at about 240 pounds on his five-foot, seven-inch frame. His stature perhaps contributed to his reflux, which in turn chronically inflamed his esophagus. He'd gotten by for years taking Prilosec or antacids, and he passed a portion of the time in his truck going through an average of a pack and a half of cigarettes a day. About six months before coming in, he began having some difficulty swallowing and actually lost close to thirty pounds. When he finally underwent evaluation, they discovered he had locally advanced esophageal cancer.

Emotionally, Phillip was still struggling, or as his daughter would say, "raging" against his loss of independence. He barely worked and needed to change his long-haul route to be available for radiation treatments. He was on board with a plan to be as aggressive as he could and, as he put it, "fuck up the cancer." All of this while trying to work enough hours to keep his health insurance benefits.

The radiation was three quarters of the way through, and the next steps included a radical neck dissection, partial glossectomy, and chemotherapy. He'd lost another twenty pounds since initiating radiation.

By the time I met Phillip, the frame of his bone structure was a greater testament to who he'd been as a person than what he'd portrayed. He felt beaten down and nearly defeated. His oncology team brought up the option of artificial feeding, but to him, the idea seemed to hit harder than his cancer diagnosis did. In Phillip's mind, a feeding tube was something old people in a nursing home had, not a fifty-two-year-old long-haul trucker who was here to "fuck up the cancer" and get back to driving.

Conversation with Phillip wasn't easy. He seethed with anger, and it took a while to get any dialogue going. I had to swear to him that I wasn't a psychiatrist, while simultaneously asserting that he was indeed not remotely crazy. What actually proved the most useful was when his tenants, Meghan and Jesús, walked in. Phillip had no biologic family that he was close to, but his relationship with the young couple was familial. They viewed him as a father, and he clearly took care of them.

Phillip was okay with them joining the conversation, so I invited them to stay. In short order, they filled the gaps in his social history and added some color with stories of practical and dirty jokes. "Poppy" was the kind of guy who could have you rolling on the floor if you weren't easily offended.

He'd thought the plan was to cure his cancer and felt that artificial feeding was a betrayal of that plan, and he was mustering to fight back. Meghan and Jesús thought of cancer as a death sentence, and none of their fears were being addressed. They weren't blood relations and, therefore, not invited to other meetings. As a result, they operated in a vacuum of fear, only receiving the limited insight Phillip could provide.

So, we began to unload some information and discussed that the oncology team had and still did view his locally advanced cancer as curable. The intent of all of this laborious life-altering treatment was to "fuck up the cancer" and get back to work. Meghan and Jesús were hearing the treatment plan for the first time and showed a mix of relief and concern regarding the impact and the idea that he wasn't in a terminal state, though Phillip still struggled to process his options and let go of the perception that a feeding tube was a personal failure.

Using their vernacular, I started to explore the proposed PEG tube. "We need to 'un-fuck' your weight loss, or things are going to get worse before they get better. Right now, there's a battleground in your throat, and we need to bypass the warzone to get food in."

I became puzzled for a moment when the long-haul trucker began talking about road construction and using different roads to deliver, then realized a PEG tube was a different road. I knew he was beginning to hear.

For the next fifteen minutes, we strategized about symptom management for energy and nausea, and I answered questions about the feeding tube. Yes, he could work if he felt up to it. No, IV nutrition was risky and not a good long-term option. Nobody would know he had a feeding tube unless he "was wearing a bikini." Meghan thought that image was really funny, and the mood continued to improve for all of us. We took the fear out of the discussion, and then Phillip could see what matched his bigger goals. The plan became to use a PEG tube and to continue with treatment.

Miriam

No two conversations about artificial nutrition are quite the same—individuals are unique, and family dynamics vary widely. Religious and cultural positions differ almost as much as a patient and their family's own interpretation of those constructs, and strokes and their impact also tend to be drastically different.

Miriam was a seventy-two-year-old moderately obese woman who lived a relatively quiet life. Her husband had passed over a decade before, and while they didn't have any children, she remained close with his sisters and extended family, though most of her social network was her church community.

Her health history included diabetes, hypertension, arthritis, and obesity. She'd been admitted to the hospital earlier in the week after preparing for a church bake sale with her friends. When they picked her up to begin preparations, they noticed that she was considerably quieter than usual, but they didn't think too much of it. The circle of friends arrived at the church and got to work. Miriam was in the back of the kitchen for a few hours preparing batter and varied delectables while her friends set up tables and chairs.

Their concern elevated when her friends found the kitchen to be a bit of a mess. If anything, Miriam was known for running the place like a precise machine. They found her seated in a chair with a facial droop and the inability to speak. Her friends said they were calling an ambulance, and reportedly, her angry gestures effectively communicated that she didn't agree with that plan. They relented and instead negotiated that they'd call her sister-in-law, Susan. When

Susan arrived, they implored Miriam to go to the hospital. Ultimately, the group got her out the back door and into Susan's car to go home, but she brought her to the hospital instead.

I came to see her a few days into her stay. She'd had an ischemic stroke, leaving her with expressive aphasia and mobility deficits. Her ability to swallow was also severely impacted, and a temporary feeding tube had been placed in her nose. To complicate matters further, she had some rectal bleeding, and a CT scan of the abdomen found a sigmoid mass. Her temporary nasal feeding tube had been placed partially to facilitate administering her bowel prep for a colonoscopy and biopsy.

When I met with her and Susan, I found Miriam to have her eyes wide open, tracking every movement I made. I introduced myself as a member of the team whose role was to help clarify her priorities in care. She nodded and shook her head appropriately in response to my questions but couldn't consistently deliver words that were clear or related to our interaction. Her attempts to communicate clearly frustrated her.

So, we resorted to head nods and shakes while trying to clarify the state of her mental capacity. Yes, it was fall. No, I'm not in New York. Yes, it was 2018. Yes, that's Susan. Yes, I'm in a hospital. No, Regan is not president.

"Is that guy on TV president?" I asked.

She gave a look of disgust, a few gesticulations, and a nod of her head. Her crisp responses strongly suggested that she had capacity. The biggest flaw in that assessment was her inability to ask me any questions in search of more information.

In the minority of cases, I was able to find power of attorney (POA) documents in the electronic medical record. In the majority, people simply never took the time to designate a POA and only verbally named a representative. In others, the document was locked at home in a fireproof safe, and people either declined to bring it in or couldn't find it. Miriam, it turned out, was a quiet but organized woman who kept things in their place. To my surprise, Susan was able to give me both POA documents, listing Susan as the POA, and an advanced directive. Things were rarely that convenient.

Goals of care conversations were almost never as black and white as an advanced directive would suggest them to be. Before exploring the documents, we needed to take the time to unpack the pertinent medical information. I began my usual line of questions to help gauge their understanding of Miriam's health status. Susan became the focus of these questions with Miriam being an active audience member. I paid close attention to her body language and expressions while often asking, "Do you understand what I'm saying? Let me say it a different way." Susan was a saint in her own capacity to seek clarification, which in turn improved her and Miriam's understanding. When clinicians meet with families, they often fail to assess the depth of information desired or the level of understanding the family already has.

Neither Miriam nor Susan were interested in learning what portion of the brain was affected or the distinctions between the modes of imaging we used to examine her deficits. They weren't seeking minutia, but rather the big picture answers: "Will she speak again? When can the tube come out of her nose? What does the mass in the colon mean? Will she walk again? Is she going to die?"

Susan noted, "Her living will says she doesn't want a feeding tube."

I endeavored to answer the questions as best as I could while also directing them to experts within the team, but conversations with team members and a review of the record did equip me to give some general answers in that case.

"You're not dying today. You've had a significant stroke, but one that can be survived. Some recovery is possible, but it's doubtful you'll get back to how you were before. Speech therapy can work with you regarding both speech and swallowing, but recovery is often slow and the end result unknown. We can work with you to see how much you can get better."

Miriam nodded her head, and Susan talked about rehab before the conversation turned back to the mass.

"The mass in your colon looks like we would expect a cancer to appear. I wish I could tell you something different." I explained that we were consulting both GI and oncology services and the oncology team wouldn't have much to say until we had a pathology specimen. Miriam had never had a colonoscopy before, so I reviewed the how and why. I let her know that the prep was often more arduous than the procedure, and no, she wouldn't feel the biopsy. "We need the biopsy so we can see what type of cancer we're dealing with and develop a treatment plan." I told them that the oncology team would give more details about staging the cancer and treatment options in the coming days. Susan asked about prognosis, and I responded by saying it was too early in the evaluation for us to be able to answer with much detail.

Eventually, we circled back to the advanced directive. In many documents, there was some common language about "terminal state" or "vegetative state" as activating triggers. That was the case here as well. I acknowledged that Miriam had a brain injury but was clearly not in a vegetative state. The previously noted gray area in these documents is the variability in how we define "terminal state." Does it mean we're dying today? This week? This month? This year? How do we factor in quality of life? I named those variations out loud while also pointing out that I didn't have a crystal ball.

Via Susan, we went on to discuss and reflect on what things historically brought joy to Miriam. The more we talked, it became clearer to all that life would be different, but many of those elements remained in reach for her.

She wasn't imminently terminal, but if her heart stopped, she didn't want CPR. If her breathing was impaired, she was open to a trial of life support but was firmly opposed to long-term ventilation. Then we moved on to the question of a feeding tube. Susan wasn't wrong in citing the check boxes of the advanced directive. It took some exploration to divine meaning from the gray area of "terminal."

Her goals so far were to try to regain functional capacities through rehab. She was invested in a diagnostic and staging workup for her colonic mass. Her advanced directive indicated "no" to artificial nutrition in a terminal or persistent vegetative state. The cancer was not yet staged and could prove to be metastatic and incurable, but her stroke was significantly limiting and might've been stimulated by the pro-embolic state cancer brings. Her initial presentation and baseline health status suggested that on the narrow end of the prognostic scale, time was measured in multiple months to more than a year without a definitive end point.

Her goals remained diagnostic workup and rehab. The use of a feeding tube maintained the possibility of rehab and potential treatment of the cancer. Miriam also had enough capacity to nod her head in approval of this idea. While we answered the question of artificial nutrition, I suspected the more important piece was the act of beginning to grasp what-if scenarios.

We acknowledged that her future was uncertain, and a great deal of valuable information was missing but anticipated. So, we planned for the best-case scenario but also took the time to identify off-ramps and decision points if things got worse. These were the nuances that weren't easily covered in an advanced directive. If Miriam's cancer became advanced, if she lost her wits, or if she was in significant pain, we'd stop artificial feeding. Susan was now the one nodding her head in understanding. We began a relationship with the first encounter, and part of the plan became to follow up with her in the clinical setting. We put this into the EMR, then got on with the work of recovery and treatment plan development.

Humphrey "Hump"

Humphrey was a Korean War veteran in his late eighties who'd had a series of three admissions in the past six months. Two of these were for pneumonia, and all three included some degree of dehydration.

He and his wife, Judith, were married a few years out of high school before he joined the services. It turned out he'd proposed to her more than once and was told no the first two times. The charm of his third attempt included a high school graduation and a tall Humphrey in a military uniform down on one knee. They started their family in increments between leave and his final return home, resulting in six children and twelve grandchildren. The family was still growing and, by the volume of visitors and phone calls, a closely connected one at that. During his younger days, Humphrey worked in the steel mills and did construction before becoming a foreman. His appetite and deep-chested laughter were apparently legend in the family. He'd been the organizer of family game night when the kids were grown and the grandchildren first began arriving.

Humphrey's health challenges included an old stroke without deficits, moderate COPD from his smoking days in the service, some anxiety which the family later understood as PTSD, and most significantly, his advanced dementia. This diagnosis formally came about five years earlier, though the family first became aware that things were off about seven years ago. During game nights of that era, Humphrey began mixing up the rules of games they'd played together for years. Even the older grandkids began to give Hump a hard time about making up games. In his early dementia, there'd been friendly jokes and excitement about "creating new games" and forgetting things, which Hump took in stride.

The family alarm bells sounded when he left the house early one morning and got escorted home after a phone call. He'd turned up at a job he had retired from twelve years previously and simply walked in and moved a desk back to an original spot. The newer employees knew something wasn't right but had no idea who he was. The foreman who'd replaced him had family experience with dementia and recognized Humphrey. He had the sense to redirect Hump, call Judith, and get him home.

The first few years were exquisitely challenging as Humphrey engaged in multiple field trips. It was a burden, but his large and loving family tackled it as best they could. They took turns checking in and keeping him engaged as well as they could.

The dark chapter was the eighteen months Humphrey spent in a locked dementia unit. During that time, Humphrey was safe but intermittently despondent at not being home. He periodically thought he was in his military barracks, and on the good days, thought of other residents as either brothers or infirmary patients. When he started struggling to walk, the prospect of field trips became less of a concern.

His family brought him home again. He'd lost about sixty pounds in two years and was no longer able to stand, even with help. He could mumble a few words and intermittently called some of his grandkids by his kids' names, but even those sparks of recognition began to fade. For months, he no longer ate or drank unless his family coaxed or hand-fed him. To their credit, Humphrey was exceptionally well cared for. It was their concerted effort that allowed him to march toward the far end of advanced dementia.

On his latest admission, we administered IV fluids and corrected his acute kidney injury. We initially covered for a urinary tract infection, but cultures were inconclusive, and we stopped his antibiotics. The unresolved problem was his limited oral intake.

Speech therapy came to see him on two different occasions. On the first visit, Humphrey was so disinterested in food that the therapist couldn't perform a safe exam. The second attempt was better in terms of his level of alertness—probably due to Judith's presence—but arguably worse in terms of outcome. His swallow was delayed, and he pocketed food. He seemed to lack a protective cough to clear the food he failed to swallow, so it had to be suctioned back out.

It was the speech therapist's note and exam that triggered the goals of care consult. She had recommended a diet of "nothing per oral" (NPO) and clarification of care goals regarding artificial feeding. Judith had heard firsthand that it was unsafe to feed him and began to dutifully notify her children about the problem.

Hump didn't have an advanced directive, and there had already been a bit of an argument over the right course of action. The diversity of strong opinions caused Judith the most distress. I gathered much of the social history in the initial encounter with her and one of her daughters, Candy. I didn't attempt to clarify a decision in that visit, but I did lay out some of what we needed to explore and recommended that we pull together some of the key members of the family to do so. We established a tentative plan for an eleven-a.m. meeting the next day. Candy took the lead in calling her siblings, and the meeting was confirmed.

The following day, I checked on Humphrey and noted that his mentation wasn't substantially different and that he was otherwise stable. After that, the social worker on my team scouted out a conference room for a meeting. As it turned out, we definitely needed a conference room. Judith and Candy were there, along with four of Humphrey's children, four adult grandchildren, and one cousin. A remaining grandson was to be conferenced in on one of their cell phones. We placed him on speaker phone in the center of the table and went through brief introductions of name and relation or title. Cathie, the beloved social worker on my team, engaged in some small talk and then sat in the middle of the family on the opposing side of the table.

I should mention that her seat choice is often intentional. She has this invaluable knack for picking up missed ques or clinical over speak as she embeds herself within the family. If I deliver information, and she observes that there's a misunderstanding or unasked question, she'll speak up and ask it from the family's perspective. Her ability to connect in a different role is an asset that can't be overstated, and it's part of the value of having a multidisciplinary team.

I began the meeting by stating that the role of palliative care was to gain a better understanding of what was going on with Humphrey and determine what he'd want us to do. Knowing that there was family discord about the decisions at hand, I acknowledged that the volume of people and engaged presence in the room was a testament to the love they had for that man. The validation helped build trust and rapport, which served to open the conversation to more informative discussion of the difficult pieces to come. I started not with the clinical story but with reciting what I'd learned of his life. I invited the family to fill in gaps and ask questions as we discussed his health concerns.

I knew of his clinical decline, but I asked them to tell me of their observations of his health trajectory over the past six months. Their answers were telling. All of them were able to speak accurately of his declining health and loss of all functional capacity. There was no denial that he was approaching the end of his life. Candy spoke up and asked if we could complete an advanced directive.

Her question provided a good opening, and I explained that unfortunately, Humphrey lacked the capacity to sign an advanced directive. The best we could do in the face of end-stage disease was imagine Humphrey with us in the room, clear-minded and understanding his state. It would be the perspective we should tackle questions from. I then detailed his clinical course as well as the cyclical nature of his admissions. We began to openly discuss his vulnerabilities as part of a slow terminal decline. One son was able to speak up and say that he felt like his dad had died a few years ago, but his body hadn't yet caught up. There were some sobs and quips about him always being late. The question about an advanced directive provided a segue to code status questions in a hypothetical way. It was quickly and unanimously established that CPR and breathing tubes were a non-starter.

I began asking my usual handful of questions. I already knew what he did for a living, but I learned that game nights and hunting trips were a couple things he did for fun. My last question regarding what the family was most worried about usually generated a need for tissues. Cathie was adept at covertly passing them to the right person, whether it was the petite granddaughter or the burly son built of his father's frame.

The answers began to flow and elucidated the differences in thoughts about Humphrey's care. They were varied, but there were often central themes the family could connect over.

"I don't want him to suffer."

"I want him to be able to come home."

His children were also worried about their mom and how she bore the weight of his care and would cope with his eventual death.

"I'm worried that he won't get better."

Judith said, "I'm so tired of him needing the hospital. I don't think this really helps him anymore."

There were a few yesses and head nods.

"I'm worried that he's in pain a lot and that he can't breathe."

The big worry came in the statement, "I don't want him to starve to death."

Cathie and I took the time to listen to these different worries and reflect them back. It was an exercise that helped me frame what I'd heard, clarify what I'd misinterpreted, and make it clear to the family that their worries were legitimate and understood.

"I'm hearing that you want him to be home, well supported, and not in pain. I'm also hearing that you're worried about his not eating." That last worry was the central decision-making point in this conversation and needed to be validated more deeply, especially when his past appetite used to be part of his identity within the family.

I took the time to acknowledge the central social and familial importance of food.

"We celebrate family around food at holidays, weddings, anniversaries, birthdays, game nights, and even funerals. If you and I don't eat, we feel hungry, and our body alerts us. Humphrey's relationship with food has become very different than ours. In end-stage dementia, there's a natural progression of the disease where we lose attentiveness to food, and our ability to swallow fades. If he has any perception of hunger, I suspect it's very different than ours. From what you've told me, he hasn't been interested in food for months. In the past, we almost reflexively recommended a feeding tube to bypass the swallowing problem. What research has shown us is that this doesn't result in people living longer, but it's often very good at reducing the anxiety of those who care for Humphrey. With end-stage dementia, though, people don't often gain weight or vitality, and it would still be a challenge for him to manage some oral secretions and reflux from a full stomach. He can't raise his hand to say, 'I'm full. Please stop.' On the chance he is interested in eating, the feeding tube will take away the pleasure of tasting it, and it doesn't really treat any symptoms. Some people with dementia pull the tubes out or have complications like clogging or infection. It's easy to place a tube, but the harder question is this: Does it really offer Humphrey anything he would want?"

There was a rich and deep discussion as the family formed and shared thoughts. I waited for a lull in the dialogue, and then suggested the alternative.

"We should always offer food. The purpose of it at this stage of life is now very different. It's not about nutrition but more about pleasure. If he's interested, we should offer it as safely as we can and accept that the natural progression of dementia is that people die from things like pneumonia or urinary tract infections. The alternative to him staying in the hospital is to provide comfort feeds and engage a team that can help focus on his comfort at home. The team I am talking about is a hospice team."

The questions shifted to asking about hospice care and whether that would help. One family member asked if that meant giving up. I reframed it to reflect the reality that we were still providing care, hoping for comfort and dignity by striving for the best possible care we could give Humphrey as he approached the end of his life. We talked about how we addressed that focus and hoped for the best in that time. Hospice care could be provided at home with the support of family. The team wasn't always there, but they were available twenty-four seven by phone. When called, they could help at a distance or come to him if needed. The care in some locations could be in a nursing home or a hospice house if the patient needed intensive support managing symptoms.

All of us had been talking for about an hour with a mix of heavy and light conversation, but it seemed like we all needed to mentally catch our breath. I restated that we had established a code status of no CPR and no intubation and were considering options of hospice care and comfort feedings or the placement of a feeding tube.

"Are there any other questions or things I should address before I step out?"

After a few clarifications, we adjourned with a plan for the family to make a decision overnight.

Candy called me a few hours later. She expressed an appreciation for our listening and taking the time to explain the options to most of them. As a group, they'd decided not to place a feeding tube and instead bring Humphrey home with the support of a hospice team. I arranged for hospice to meet with Judith and Candy the next day. I had the sense that we sent that family home cared for and intact.

Over the past few years, my colleagues in other disciplines have become more adept at identifying evidence-based reasons not to pursue artificial feeding in end-stage dementia. Some gastroenterologists are evaluating the valuable question of "should we" with as much weight as "can we." There's an ongoing cultural shift away from the procedural care I encountered when my career began. A recent speech therapy note in a similar patient actually included the following research citation:

PEG tube use in dementia does not reduce aspiration and prevent the pneumonia to which patients with dementia so often succumb; aspiration from oral and gastric secretions continues unabated. Feeding tubes do not extend survival. PEG tubes in dementia, research shows, increases not only morbidity, but also mortality. PEG tube placement often requires concomitant use of physical or chemical restraints, exacerbating discomfort, increasing the risk of pressure sores, and further compromising patient comfort and human dignity. PEG tube placement does not extend and may actually shorten life. Not only are there no long-term proven benefits, but short-term survival may be reduced after placement.[30]

---

[30] C. Mueller et al., *Aspen Adult Nutrition Support Core Curriculum* 39, no. 3 (2017): Ethics and Law.

Goals of Care

In my inpatient practice, the main reason for consultation is to assist the larger team in clarifying the patient's goals of care. This request may pertain to the present admission and decisions at hand or preferences for future treatment and readmission. It may develop when there are family conflicts or confusion as to how best navigate significant decisions when the patient's capacity is tenuous. The influence of family in decision-making often gains power when a patient is at their weakest and most vulnerable state. My ethical duty is to the patient first, while my hope is that I can still bring the family unit together in favor of the patient's treatment preferences.

My team is fortunately blessed with highly skilled people from diverse disciplines. I've mentioned our social worker, but I also need to mention our counselor, Donna. She has a depth of experience and educates us regularly from the lens of trauma-informed care. A palliative care consultation, whether symptom management, goals clarification, or both, is also a therapeutic encounter. Donna is instrumental in following up extensively with patients and families after we unearth the struggles they're dealing with. As clinical specialists of many disciplines, we bring different resources to the table, but the value of those resources may change in relation to the patient's health status.

Larissa

Larissa and I met a few years into her battle with cancer. At sixty-two, Larissa had had a relationship with dance from her youth all the way to her adulthood. She worked a mix of retail jobs, but the role she most identified with was dance teacher. For a while, she had owned her own business, serving community kids and enriching those she encountered. She was gregarious by nature, and dance was both art and a chance to endlessly talk with and teach people. Unfortunately, she'd also been having a multi-decade long dance with cigarettes.

Larissa had some luck—of sorts—a few years ago as the health system began advocating for early screening for lung cancer in those at higher risk. Some chest imaging had identified a spiculated mass in her right lung. The early diagnosis led to lung resection and local radiation for early stages, and she'd remained disease free for nearly five years. Her diagnosis had been life-changing when combined with her previously undiagnosed COPD. With a partial lobectomy, her pulmonary function was diminished to the extent that shouting dance directions to her students was taking most of her air, but she flatly refused to wear supplemental oxygen in the studio. She was grateful to be alive and continued to be a presence in the dance community in different ways.

A persistent cough and some intermittent hemoptysis brought her back to her oncologist about seventeen months ago. That time, her left lung was the culprit, presenting a new cancer. Treatment began with cisplatin chemotherapy and was followed by weight loss and unrelenting nausea. She had some initial response to treatment, even as dosing was reduced, but peripheral neuropathy had dulled the sensation in her feet to the extent that she described herself as having two leaded left feet. The combined radiation therapy, loss of appetite, and anemia all conspired to steal her energy and reduce her spirit.

Repeated chest CT scans did little to lift her spirit. Disease progression, despite the rigors and demands of treatment, was a very difficult outcome to bear. Some dehydration and pancytopenia led to a hospital admission out of an abundance of caution. I saw her at the point of transition from first-line chemotherapy to second-line treatment due to growing intolerance. Donna and I met her and made her husband, Mitch's, acquaintance as he joined us.

Early in the conversation, it became very clear that Larissa was focused on further treatment in hopes of pushing back the cancer's progression. Since her goals were clear, the focus of the conversation naturally shifted to symptom management. She had things she wanted to see and do relating to the studio, so we explored the options. For her neuropathy, we discussed gabapentin as an option to reduce the tingling in her legs. We started with three hundred milligrams at bedtime with a plan to increase over time.

She was also having trouble sleeping, which impacted her energy levels, and she felt like when she was awake, she was not fully awake, often finding herself napping. We started with fifteen milligrams of Remeron at bedtime, hoping for an appetite boost along with the ability to sleep easier. Fatigue was her predominant complaint, and I worried that the Neurontin (gabapentin) would also have her drowsy as she adjusted to it. She just didn't have the energy she used to, even with abbreviated and modified days. We agreed to trial a stimulant as an outpatient with five milligrams of Ritalin after breakfast and lunch. We planned on starting this after she was discharged because being energized while hospitalized wasn't as valuable to her.

Larissa named Mitch as her representative. Her code status was full code. Since she hadn't taken the time to fill out an advanced directive, I recommended that she take some time to contemplate that and the power of attorney paperwork. The next day, Donna and I came by for a follow-up of her symptoms and to give her the blank documents. We had a palliative care clinic linked with the oncology service, so I connected her with them and wished her well. She was discharged after receiving IV fluids and a blood transfusion.

Three months passed before I saw Larissa again. When my team was consulted, I recognized the name, and the details of her story clicked back into place as I read the social pieces about dance. She'd continued with chemotherapy and had a positive response to symptom management. For a few months, she had intermittently made it back to the dance studio and officiated a few competitions. There wasn't a new staging CT scan to review, but her presenting pulmonary status was concerning.

I met Larissa and Mitch at her bedside in the ICU. Her smile remained, but a mild panicked look replaced her gregariousness. She struggled to breathe and required the support of Optiflow™ to maintain adequate oxygenation. Her chest x-ray showed an opacity in the left lung, forming the diagnosis of post-obstructive pneumonia. The CT result from the ER showed involvement of her mediastinal lymph nodes and a measurable increase in her lung mass. The cancer was compressing smaller air passages, leading to this pneumonia.

Antibiotics and steroids were ordered, and radiation oncology was consulted to weigh in on focal treatment to the offending portion of her lung mass. I recommended one to two milligrams of IV morphine as needed for her dyspnea.

The ICU team agreed, and she visibly responded to her first dose. While I waited for her nurse to administer the IV, I briefly revisited some goals of care questions, affirming that medical management was the plan. As I inquired about code status, I stated that her future was unknown, and her breathing status had her worried. Progressing cancer wasn't an ideal time for a relaxed, fully informative conversation about code status. She'd accept a limited trial of ventilation if it became necessary, but was less interested in the option of CPR if death came. When she looked to Mitch, he answered for her, and she remained full code.

At about 4:00 a.m., Larissa's struggle to breathe became more apparent. She switched to a BiPAP mask, and shortly after that, the team decided to intubate and sedate her. Mitch hadn't left the ICU during the night. Donna made it to the hospital before me and was supporting him.

When I arrived mid-morning, I checked in with the ICU team and then sat down with Mitch. He was bleary-eyed, exhausted, and overwhelmed. I gave him simplified updates on her status—presently stable but in respiratory failure. She was in some shock, requiring a single pressor, and likely dehydrated when she came in, but IVF replacement allowed us to reduce her pressor dependence.

I shared that the team's short-term plans were to keep her sedated, let her rest, and treat the pneumonia. I told him there were no decisions to be made that day and that he should go home, eat something, and sleep. It would be more important for him to be there in support when we reduced the sedation in an effort to wean her from ventilator support. I confirmed his cell number, and he took the nursing station number on the back of my card before going home for the day.

Fortunately, the next day, she showed some progress in her pulmonary status. We were able to lighten her sedation, and she managed spontaneous modes of ventilation without needing high levels of oxygen support. She'd responded to IVF and antibiotics and no longer needed a pressor. Later that afternoon, we were able to move from the ventilator to Optiflow^{tm} support. The pertinent question of the moment was asking her what she'd want us to do if she failed to breathe adequately without the ventilator. Should we put it back in?

She had capacity to answer the question, and that time she didn't look to Mitch for approval. "No. I don't want that tube again."

We clarified that critical care support would be ongoing, but if her breathing failed, we could shift priorities toward making her comfortable and allow death. It took a bit more time to convey that CPR would not be performed, as the intervention most commonly comes with intubation. We focused on symptomatic concerns and then adjourned the meeting for the day.

I followed up with a third visit to find Larissa breathing much better. Her oxygen requirements were again coming down, and she was back to nasal cannula oxygen. She'd made some intermittent use of morphine for dyspnea near bedtime, and it resulted in a decent night's sleep. We spent that visit doing some advanced care planning.

Part of the shortcomings of clarifying goals of care was that what we documented didn't always carry forward beyond the hospital stay. Larissa affirmed her desired code status but had nothing to reflect that at home. In Pennsylvania, we had a form called Pennsylvania Orders for Life Sustaining Treatment, or POLST for short. Other states had out-of-hospital do not resuscitate (DNR) orders or Medical Orders for Life Sustaining Treatment (MOLST). In Pennsylvania, it was a bright pink form we could complete that translated advanced directives, living wills, or, most importantly, conversation into orders. We checked the box for DNR along with the box supporting limited medical intervention. That choice excluded intubation but allowed rehospitalization.

I made copies for the electronic medical record and gave her the original and a copy. She remained invested in further treatment, so I affirmed a plan for her to follow up with her oncologist at a later time. My team would work with her in the outpatient clinic for symptom management or even at her home if travel became too difficult. Four days later, she was discharged. I heard through the team that further treatment was considered high risk and that she signed on with a home hospice team.

Maria

Maria was seventy-eight and presented to the hospital from a skilled local nursing facility. She arrived with her husband, Dwight, and their daughter, Janet, and was checked in by speaker phone during our consultation. Maria had been a resident of the nursing home for the past six years, a different phase of her nearly fifty-eight-year-long marriage. Dwight seemed to be enjoying a social renaissance in his role as care giver.

Maria wasn't particularly aware of the conversation but would intermittently give a smile when not puzzling over her oxygen tubing. She was on the tail-end decline of advanced dementia, and because her family was well aware of this, code status was already pre-established. She had some mild COPD but was able to eat with assistance and still spent a portion of the day out of bed in a reclining chair—she hadn't walked in over a year. When she came to us, she had a fever and elevated white blood cell count.

Maria's chest x-ray showed concerning signs of pneumonia, so we started her on antibiotics. The initial films raised a question of a middle-right lobe lung mass, so a follow-up CT scan was ordered. Getting Maria to lie still for the imaging was a challenge and ultimately required some light sedation. The palliative care team was consulted to clarify goals of care, with the lung mass likely being cancer.

The conversation was surprisingly light as I gathered social history and medical history. They were a highly educated family that had come to terms with where Maria was on her terminal decline.

They took the news of the CT findings in stride with a mix of disappointment and a great deal of curiosity.

The hospital team presented the idea of performing a biopsy to formally diagnose that it was indeed cancer. Oncology had not yet been consulted as there wouldn't be much to discuss in the absence of pathology results. The family's state of curiosity had them favoring a biopsy, but it was unclear if this would be obtainable by bronchoscopy or CT guidance.

Before we got to discussing the option of biopsy, I took the time to learn Maria's story as much as I could. So, I asked the family one of my standard questions: "What are you worried about the most?"

The husband and daughter both answered that they didn't want her to suffer at that stage of life. We'd already affirmed some advanced directives such as no CPR, no intubation, and no artificial feeding earlier in our conversation.

Without direct input from oncology, I had my suspicions that chemotherapy and immunotherapy were unlikely to be offered, as she lacked the capacity to report symptoms or understand treatment. Even palliative radiation would prove difficult with her aversion to lying flat or still. As I began sharing that concern, both Dwight and Janet began speaking over each other, stating she wouldn't want such interventions.

I also mentioned that she wouldn't be able to share any potential symptoms she might have relating to the treatment. They agreed with that.

So, I raised the question, "We could do a biopsy, but how would the information be useful to Mary? It wouldn't inform treatment options, and there are risks to her safety and comfort if we do."

I could see Dwight struggling to reconcile his desire to know and heard Janet on speaker say, "Oh."

They needed a moment to think, so I simply restated the current plan of care outside of the biopsy option.

As they thought, I considered a possible route that had been suggested to me a while ago by a colleague, Dr. Dan R. In similar decision dilemmas, he pointed out that there was a completely safe way to satisfy curiosity without risk to the patient. If a biopsy wouldn't be used to guide treatment, it could be obtained during an autopsy. Dwight and Jane made a decision before I had to ponder using that approach.

They wanted her pneumonia treated but didn't wish to pursue a lung biopsy. They were curious—but not that curious—so we talked further about treatment goals beyond that particular hospital stay. They wished for her to return to the nursing home where the staff already knew Mary and wanted her to stay comfortable in that setting. We next explored the option of hospice care and whether future hospitalization would serve her well. Thinking perhaps back to the need to sedate her for the recent CT scan, they decided that rehospitalization might not serve her needs in the best manner, and they opted to explore hospice care.

Juggernaut

Dictionaries define the term Juggernaut as a huge, powerful, and overwhelming force or institution. In pop-culture, "The Juggernaut" is also a fictional character created in the world of Marvel Comics. He's one of immense physical strength and often single-minded focus and has the capacity to walk, jog, run, and pick up momentum to batter through walls unscathed and continue unslowed. The character can lift mountains and throw buildings. In later versions, he wears a metal helmet to block external influences upon his mindset.[31]

Our healthcare institutions often wield powerful forces over life and death, sometimes while ignoring information outside of the patient-level problems at hand. I've witnessed various iterations of the juggernaut phenomenon in clinical practice over the course of my career. The walking phase typically begins with a well-intended consult request from one discipline to another. I've mentioned before that in palliative medicine, it's important to have the broader picture of a patient and their surrounding world to begin the exploration of goals of care. Sometimes, information is incomplete, or rapidly changing circumstances necessitate seeking the input of different experts.

Healthcare providers are a diverse group of skilled people who each bring components of their chosen discipline and self to the care of the patients we serve. As we call in a specialist, we're specifically

[31] "Juggernaut (Comics)," Wikipedia, Wikimedia Foundation, last modified July 19, 2021, https://en.wikipedia.org/wiki/Juggernaut_(comics)

requesting their specialized knowledge and the tools of their trade. That specialized focus has the tendency to act as partial blinder, much like the juggernaut's metal helmet impedes external influence. This is, of course, a generalization, but I'd posit that the specialist is biased in favor of focusing more intently on the problem they were called to address than the whole picture of the patient and their story.

To expand on the concept of the specialist, we'd be unlikely to call upon a surgeon to address psychologic trauma, but more likely to request their expertise in managing skeletal trauma. Their focus is on the physical, and their tool is surgical intervention. In a reverse of this example, the scalpel wielded by the trauma counselor is their knowledge of the human psyche, the effect of traumatic experiences, and the act of counseling. Each clinician is highly skilled but very different in the tools they possess and how they wield them.

A less contrasting example would be consultants addressing a patient presenting with complaints of abdominal pain. There's clinical evaluation and decision-making, but respective disciplines would engage this through their respective biases. The colorectal surgeon may be more apt to look at imaging and offer surgical interventions, whereas a gastroenterologist would be biased in favor of seeking additional information and intervention through endoscopy. This isn't to say that either discipline is completely blind to the idea or incapable of recommending a different specialist if their tools are clearly a poor fit. Most of us collaborate a great deal.

The progressive and interlinked approaches to care very often change what would be a dismal and brief disease process to a positive and thriving outcome. Perhaps the most challenging skill to learn across disciplines is restraint.

Imagine having a hard-earned and practiced skill honed to the highest level of expertise that over decades of practice has become both an element of deep pride and a substantial component of your self-identity. It takes additional skill to be called upon to use your specialized tool and say no. "No, my tool—sharp and polished—doesn't serve this patient. No, my tool, while desired and requested directly by the patient and my colleagues, doesn't fit."

I'm often called upon by specialists who recognized that their tool doesn't fit, even though they themselves constructed the trap of offering it. Then the clinician, upon constructing this fine trap, steps directly into it because our patient wants a specialist to use this offered tool.

In defense of each specialist, sometimes it's the colleague who builds the false offering, then invites them into the care of the patient. It's easy and thorough to consult a specialist, but more difficult to say why it might be problematic. It's hard to say, "No, I have the right tool, but the circumstances are wrong."

The following is a story of well-intended care that became the subliminal evil of the juggernaut.

Isadora

Isadora was seventy-three and the mother of five children. She'd been widowed for the past five years and spent the preceding fourteen caring for her husband who'd been debilitated by a stroke. She'd moved from Puerto Rico in the 1980s and was residing alone at that point in time. Her children were supportive, with her daughter Fernanda calling multiple times a day. She'd been an active woman both with raising her then-grown children and in caring for her husband.

The result of time on the human body was reducing her physical capacity but not her mental sharpness. She could walk through her apartment but ventured out less and less. Many of her meals were frozen dinners prepared in the microwave, but her children delivered some food and checked in with her between the demands of their work and younger families. Isadora had turned down offers to move in with Fernanda.

She'd been a smoker for a portion of her life, but fortunately, cancer was never to become part of her story. Through vigilance or some other reason, in April 2016, she underwent chest imaging. It didn't show cancer but did reveal a thoracoabdominal aneurysm. Out of an abundance of concern, her primary care provider made the dutiful referral to cardiothoracic surgery (CT surgery) for evaluation. She went to that first meeting with her daughter.

In 2016, her health status placed her as a moderate risk for the potentially major step of surgical repair of her aneurysm. Fortunately for her, the deep expertise of the CT surgeon culminated in a recommendation of watchful waiting. It was of a small enough span that surgery wasn't the recommended intervention. She returned home and continued about her business. Over time, her body wore down further, and she accepted the assistance of family.

In June 2017, she came back to her primary care provider's office. She'd been following up for management of her high blood pressure and efforts to maintain her depleting kidney function. On that particular visit, she complained of some back and abdominal pain that was becoming moderate in its intensity. Her PCP wasted no time and promptly sent her for imaging.

The imaging didn't provide hopeful news. Her thoracoabdominal aneurysm had expanded considerably but was mercifully without evidence of rupture, though it was undoubtedly the source of her back and abdominal pain. She was sent back to the CT surgeon.

What followed was a series of office visits with family and documented presentations of the risks and benefits of surgical intervention. Clear language detailed the risk of progression and potential rupture of the aneurysm if she didn't accept the recommendation for surgical intervention.

In May of 2017, she left the last visit with her CT surgeon making the statement that she should go home and think about surgery. Her aneurysm measured 6.2 centimeters, and the plan was to return to the office to discuss her decision. She missed that appointment and declined a number of phone calls. Through the diligence of the surgical team, she did finally answer a call and agreed to come back.

With some amazement, I noted that the follow-up appointment was in November of 2018. She sat down in front of the surgeon who'd consistently recommended surgical intervention and had the fortitude to speak her mind. She'd come to the appointment to formally decline. It didn't appear that any back-up plan or advanced care planning would follow. She simply went home without a formal plan while clearly expressing that it would not be surgery.

While outpatient documentation didn't reveal an advanced care plan, it did appear that Isadora had a plan in her own mind. A month later, she called a cab and presented to the ER with worsening abdominal and back pain, rightly attributing it to her aneurysm. She didn't believe surgical intervention was an option at that point and made a simple, direct, and clear request to her ER doctor: "I'm here for hospice."

Documented discussion reiterated her request and further affirmed that she understood the source of her pain and was seeking help with symptom management. She clarified her code status was to be DNR and do not intubate (DNI).

With any ER admission, there are a myriad of activities that occur in tandem. They took her history, did a physical exam, and completed admitting paperwork, lab work, and imaging. Isadora was pulled into the institutional machine the moment she painfully walked through the automatic sliding glass doors. The juggernaut stirred.

Being winter, it was flu season, and a component of her complaint was chest pain. As part of routine lab work, a respiratory viral panel was added on. While these labs were being processed, the ER team consulted hospice. Isadora was seen by a hospice liaison in the ER and accepted to the inpatient hospice unit. Being accepted to an inpatient hospice unit required either an acute pain crisis or the perception that life expectancy might be measured in days to a week.

While those arrangements were being made, a strange thing happened: That woman with an expanding thoracoabdominal aneurysm had a comparatively trivial lab finding. Her respiratory viral panel returned positive for RSV-B—she had an expanding aneurysm and a cold. The ER team, being thorough, presented that to her and asked if she'd like to be admitted for supportive management of her viral respiratory infection. She accepted the offer. The juggernaut groaned, sat up, arched its back, and stretched its mighty arms.

The hospice plan was put on hold, and they admitted her to a hospital bed with full capacity to navigate medical decisions. Her family was notified of her admission and came to visit. The following morning, she had a non-contrast CT of the chest due to a concern that the aneurysm was hemorrhaging.

Later that day, her attending physician presented the findings to her and offered emergency CT surgery intervention. In the same note, the doctor documented that her "ultimate goal was to be kept comfortable in the process of dying and not undergo surgery."

The patient both understood the offer and the steadily approaching consequence of consistently refusing surgery over the past two years. The hospitalist had the foresight to document, "The patient also makes statements indicating that her family is divided regarding surgery versus non-surgical care." The juggernaut grinned.

At about ten in the evening, her family was called in to meet with a tired, uncomfortable, and vulnerable Isadora and her medical team. Picture a dying woman seated in bed, the sense of urgency tangible as five family members and a medical team discussed the steps available to treat her aneurysm. There was a palpable imbalance of power, and Isadora conceded and agreed to a CT surgery consult. The juggernaut stretched its powerful legs and began a slow, heavy stroll.

Isadora was transferred to the surgical intensive care unit where pre-operative orders began to populate her chart. The next morning, her CT surgeon met with her and her family and requested that she change her code status to full code. Isadora consented to further diagnostic workup but refused to change her code status. A contrast CT scan was ordered to further assess changes in her aneurysm and better determine if bleeding was a concern since earlier imaging had shown signs of the possibility. The imaging showed that it stretched from her aortic arch down into the abdominal space. The juggernaut steadied its stride.

While there had been a recent hemorrhage, there was no active bleeding at the time of the imaging. However, the family discord was hemorrhaging into the hallway. Fernanda and her brother Guillermo had completed a Five Wishes advanced directive with Isadora as she came into the ICU. The document had affirmed code status of no CPR and no intubation. Isadora's brother Gustavo had just arrived from the airport with fragmented updates and was vocally in favor of all available options. The juggernaut shrugged its rippling shoulders and strolled on.

Later in the day, Isadora underwent a thoracentesis which evacuated some bloody drainage and improved her breathing. A pigtail catheter was placed to manage further drainage. She was increasingly anxious, and her underlying COPD didn't help her ability to breathe. She was repeatedly asked her wishes regarding code status and consistently declined to change it. The desire for hospice care and symptom management were behind the juggernaut, and it walked on, picking up speed.

Sometime around two in the morning, Gustavo and Isadora met with both CT surgery and pulmonary critical care over her complaints of dyspnea. In the dark of the night, she relented, and her code status was changed to full code. Because she was having difficulty breathing and was so anxious early the next morning, her family begged for help in managing her symptoms. She received some morphine for her dyspnea and some Xanax for extra control of her anxiety. Within the hour, she was no longer lucid or able to hold a conversation beyond moans. A shiny trap had been constructed, and the juggernaut began to jog. She'd still never consented to surgery despite the endless prompts.

The palliative care team was consulted to help clarify goals of care. I arrived to find a visibly uncomfortable and fully encephalopathic Isadora in bed with Fernanda at the bedside. I recapped what I knew of her story and listened to her concerns. Fernanda rightly observed that her mother was suffering and that she just wanted her to be comfortable. She also informed me of some differences in opinion between her brother, the patient's brother, and the three siblings. We were no longer in a position to discuss Isadora's wishes with Isadora. Had she not made those clear, though? The juggernaut jogged on, undeterred.

The CT surgery team ordered an additional CT scan and diagnosed findings of an extensive mural thrombus. Her renal function was deteriorating, and in reality, she was dying. The medical machine was moving, and Isabella transitioned from being a moderate surgical risk the year before to a very high surgical risk. The surgical team pulled me aside, voicing concerns that the family wanted surgery. Irony didn't faze the juggernaut, and it began to run.

I could build a case from the record that Isadora didn't want the heroic intervention that was being offered. Unfortunately, that had been well documented for years, and those wielding their polished surgical tools had been asked to come. It was incredibly difficult to pull back your expertise and close your toolbox when you possessed what was previously the right tool and found it being asked for with urgency.

The CT surgical team asked the cardiology team to see her and evaluate her for surgical risk. Specifically, the team was exploring for coronary artery disease or perhaps a reason to stop the juggernaut.

But it sprinted full force through walls, and a cardiac catheterization was scheduled for the next morning. Nephrology was consulted regarding her kidney function and potential post-surgical dialysis need. The ground shook with the juggernaut's footfall.

The chart also documented a family meeting to occur at nine a.m. the next morning. Not for the first time, I found that even though there was a family meeting, no other team was coming. Even though I didn't set it up, I would definitely be there. I took charge of making sure all family decision-makers would be coming.

I arrived at the bedside at 8:45 a.m. to find Isadora moaning and still encephalopathic. She could open her eyes when I called her name and briefly focus, but meaningful conversation was way beyond her now. The cardiac catheterization was scheduled for the morning whenever her case became next. Documentation in the chart suggested possible operative repair of her expanding thoracoabdominal aneurysm by afternoon. On a typical day, the surgical teams would already be in the operating room, so I wasn't surprised that the family meeting had become mine.

Nine in the morning came and went, and my anxiety level rose as I realized the family hadn't arrived yet. The juggernaut crashed through the door in the form of a transport stretcher and patient escort.

Shit!

Watching as the stretcher and attendant wove between people, isolation carts, and visitors down the too-short hallway gave me a few beats to agonize over what the right thing to do might be. Fernanda, Guillermo, and three other siblings arrived twenty paces behind the stretcher. Two of them passed it and entered the room while Fernanda and Guillermo stopped to speak with me. The juggernaut was at Isadora's door.

I expressed a sense of urgency to them that we really did need to make a decision right then and there.

Fernanda spoke first. "It's difficult, but we need to honor my mother's wishes and not do surgery."

Transport maneuvered the stretcher, and in doing so, positioned the remaining siblings back in the hall where they joined the conversation.

"I just want to keep her comfortable."

Isadora's nurse was standing just behind me, nodding her head as the conversation unfolded. I asked her to excuse patient transport and halt the mounting effort to move her to the stretcher.

We clarified that the goals of care were comfort focused. I observed that if we drew lab work and did CT scans, we'd continue to find abnormal things—things that we were past expecting to fix—and should stop looking. They agreed that the cardiac catheterization wasn't useful and supported the idea of reengaging the hospice team that she'd walked in seeking.

I notified the various team members who'd been called upon for their expertise. There was a universal expression of relief that we wouldn't be continuing our workup or planning surgery.

Each team member, with the best intentions, had added momentum to the very juggernaut they wished to avoid. By the narrowest of margins, we sidestepped the goliath and managed to resume the care she initially sought. I hated considering what would've happened if the stretcher came at 8:25 a.m. or the family at 9:45 a.m.

Isadora died three days later, comfortable and attended by family. The juggernaut lumbered on elsewhere in the hospital.

Nancy: "I Don't Want Nobody Cutting on Me"

Palliative medicine was consulted to see Nancy, and the request read, "Goals of care: patient refusing everything." Nancy was seventy-two and presented to a rural network hospital with signs of heart failure. This was her second stay in about a year's time for a similar complaint. She'd become short of breath while walking into her apartment, and normal daily activity had become increasingly challenging. The source of her heart failure was mitral valve regurgitation.

In the past, she'd been seen at her hometown hospital and received some IV diuresis and control of arrhythmia. She had considerable ankle edema and required oxygen support at rest on arrival. The receiving hospital was concerned enough about her heart failure that they had her life flighted down for higher level management and evaluation for mitral valve replacement. At over twelve thousand dollars for most flights, it was no small step.

I met Nancy's nurse in the hallway, and she gave me some background of the events leading up to the consult. Nancy was pissed, distrustful, questioning every medication, and refusing some. She'd rebuffed a repeat EKG, noting that she had one the day before at the other hospital. She declined a planned echocardiogram to better evaluate valvular concerns and function. The yelling started when she was told she couldn't have breakfast because the team was deciding whether she might have a cardiac catheterization later. She flatly rejected further labs at that point. Somewhere, we'd either done a poor job of explaining what we offered or a poor job of listening to what she wanted.

When I met with Nancy, she was obviously not in a tolerant mood.

It took some convincing, but I said, "I'm here to try to understand you better so we can take care of you the way you want us to. I'm not here to tell you what to do."

She gave me a cold stare. "Are you a head doctor? A shrink?"

"No, I'm not. And nobody thinks you're nuts." I had to meet her where she was and acknowledge her anger and distrust. I got the sense that I stood on a very thin line, and if I gave the impression of nudging her to do something, I'd get thrown out of the room pretty quickly.

"Continue."

"How are you feeling right now?"

"Pissed."

"I get that. Tell me how your breathing feels now."

"Crappy. I huff when I have to get up."

I asked, "Is it worse, the same, or better than yesterday?"

"It's about the same, maybe a little better."

We did a light review of systems, then I asked, "Have you had heart failure symptoms before?"

"Yes, but like a year ago, and I didn't have to come here then."

"How long did it take before you started feeling bad?"

"Weeks. I felt a little worse each day. Maybe I waited too long to see my doctor. He just sent me to the hospital, and then I ended up here."

I used this as an opening to shift the conversation out of the medical realm a bit as I really didn't know Nancy yet. "Who's your support network back home? Who helps you when you have health problems or just helps out in general?"

With this shift in focus, her guard came down a bit, and she talked. She lived alone after a divorce, and her ex had remained a friend until he died after a work incident. She expressed some bitterness over how he was treated after his injury. I suspected that she cared for him some afterward, and his work injury and that experience played a role in her approach to medical care. Her core network were her sisters and her ex's sister, plus an assortment of nieces and nephews. It seemed most of them lived up and down the same stretch of streets surrounding the room she rented—not really an apartment the way she described it. She'd worked as a waitress at a variety of places and, in semi-retirement, still took some holiday weeks because "tips are better then."

I gradually shifted the conversation back to the medical side and assessed what she understood of her health status. "So, tell me. What are you hearing from the medical team here about your health concerns?"

I could see her bristle a bit at the question. "The valves in my heart are leaking fluid, and it's going to my legs."

I said I could give her more detail about the mitral valve that seemed to be the source of the problem and how it was leading to her shortness of breath and fluid retention. Medical literacy was not her strong suit, but I did the best I could to find simple layman explanations for her problem. The larger clinical team was also trying to get a more complete understanding of her cardiac function.

She was appreciative of the time I took to speak with her and further explore her valvular heart disease. The purpose for this admission was an evaluation for valve replacement surgery while optimizing her present status.

I utilized her growing trust to ask the dangerous question. "Help me understand why you're refusing some of the diagnostic testing."

Her answer was about as clear as one could hope for. "Nobody said anything about cutting on me."

It turns out that with all of our high-level technology and capacity for exquisitely skilled surgical intervention, we'd completely neglected the most basic of tasks: communication. The medical team had formulated a plan to transfer her for optimization and evaluation for valve replacement surgery, but nobody had informed the owner of Nancy's body, i.e., Nancy, about the option of surgical intervention. I couldn't blame her for not trusting the medical team much at that point.

I affirmed that she had a right to be pissed regarding the late communication and all of the otherwise valid care steps that occurred before of it. So, we began to look for common ground in her current care concerns, some of which were easier to establish. She did want to be able to breathe better and fit into her normal shoes again. We were able to clarify that it meant saying yes to most medication. I pointed out that our approach to diuresis could cause electrolyte disturbances that lab work might help us identify and mitigate. She'd become agreeable to lab work, and the progress continued.

She was pretty adamant about not wanting any invasive diagnostics. For the time being, the cardiac catheterization was canceled. However, she did agree that development of chest pain or lab concerns (showing a troponin spike) would cause her to reconsider, and the option should be revisited if that occurred. I shared with her that I accepted her position and would convey it to the extended team so they could better appreciate where she stood. I also mentioned that I was worried that over time her heart failure may worsen and irreversible changes might occur.

Ultimately, Nancy didn't pursue valve replacement surgery. She was accepting of the occasional decompensation of heart function into outright failure. For the time being, she found the option of hospitalization in her community hospital near family and friends to be a far superior option to a sudden and unplanned surgical adventure. In short, she wanted to go home and think about it. She spoke more with cardiology, and that became the plan. We also clarified code status as full code and identified a representative if she were to lose the ability to speak for herself.

For me, that would've been case closed—and a relatively straightforward one—if it weren't for my epiphany the next day. I found myself pulled to a different hospital, sitting in an office, and working on a laptop while in front of a monitor with a camera. The office was affiliated with the ICU, and the intensivist used the screen and camera to connect to any of our ICUs via telemedicine carts or room-based cameras. When the IT specialist came in to make some adjustments to the monitor, it hit me.

The entire conversation I held with Nancy could've easily been from one hundred miles away—from across the planet, really. The consult, at its core, was a conversation. One source of her anxiety was the separation from her family and being in a whole new hospital by herself. I could've easily done that entire consult from my location to a hospital that didn't have a palliative medicine consult service. The care would've been better while the results would've been the same. If she'd desired intervention beyond what her hometown hospital could provide, then we would've set things in motion. In the absence of that, she would've had better, more efficient care without an unnecessary twelve-thousand-dollar flight.

That consult was the birthplace of an idea that grew into the palliative telemedicine service.

Palliative Telemedicine

The telemedicine program in my network is robust and includes multiple disciplines across many communities and affiliated hospitals. When a call came out from the telemedicine leadership team seeking input on any new and innovative practice areas that might utilize telemedicine, I jumped at the opportunity to share my observation. But there was apprehension about doing something new and different when we broached the topic. The underlying theme of the conversation was, “Please don’t talk to the telemedicine people. They might want to do it.”

It was with cautious and anxious blessing that I eventually met with our telemedicine team. Change is rarely a simple or linear process, and it took a good deal of time for institutional anxiety to evolve into investment in a concept. In reality, I effectively stepped outside of the network to work on quantifying the need for a telemedicine program. This became the purpose for doctoral research, which in turn gathered evidence supporting the need for a telemedicine program in the rural palliative care vacuum. One degree, a paper, a poster, and a TED talk later, things began to slowly move forward.

A year before the COVID-19 pandemic began, we launched our palliative telemedicine consult service in the ICU at one of our three rural hospitals.

Many components of palliative telemedicine consultation are the same as in-person consultation, though a few are starkly different. The similarities are the need for active listening, assessing the patient’s and family’s knowledge deficits, and learning about their fears, values, and related goals. Much of consultation consists of translating the language of multiple specialties into layman's terms for the purpose of making sense. Once a patient and family understand the health circumstances and available options, then you can sort through them.

As with many ICU consults, the patient is often without capacity or voice. Assessing lung sounds, heart sounds, vitals, skin, edema, responsiveness, and general frailty can be done remotely. The conversation may be by video at the bedside with family or by phone. If by phone, there's not much difference between an in-person or telemedicine consult. If by video, I explain why I'm not present and that this mode is really the best option to make this important dialogue a possibility. I have yet to have a family or patient who didn't appreciate—or worse, resented—the option of telemedicine.

The more significant practice differences only became apparent with increased experience. With in-person consults, there's informal conversation with nursing staff, speech therapy, physical therapy, respiratory therapists, or even pastoral care before I step into the room. All the valuable information that might not belong on the official chart may be communicated in that informal frame. The nurse might tell me that the wife visited and argued with the ex-wife, while the surprised fiancée cried at the bedside. The detailed, important, messy, and complicated information is unlikely to be in print but certainly has a bearing on the patient's well-being and related decision-making.

In an in-person consult, there's often a need for family to follow me outside to express a concern or ask questions they were too uncomfortable to ask in front of the patient. I often make a point of pausing outside the room and starting a note to allow for this informal conversation.

In telemedicine, I need to make a conscious effort to speak with nursing on the phone first to ask for any backstory or hand over a virtual business card to the family after the meeting. I want to have the missing information and convey my accountability to them and their loved one.

With this system, I'm also dependent on having a presenter who can remotely wheel in the camera cart and do things like auscultate lung and heart sounds or move bandages and linen for assessment. The cart consists of a monitor screen, where I'm visible, and a speaker. It's also equipped with a connected stethoscope for auscultation, and my camera is high definition with great zooming capability. The setup stands about shoulder height. With many different teams doing telemedicine consultation, the demand for and availability of the cart has been the largest time-consuming problem. With in-person consultation, on most occasions, I simply walk in when ready. That kind of flexibility is somewhat reversed with telemedicine. The remote hospital is ready for you when they're ready for you.

The other stark difference, which I'll detail in the next story, relates to control over the meeting, especially my limited control over where I "sit." I may not be closest to the patient or able to move as the flow of conversation dictates. For all the technology that may come with telemedicine platforms, I'm still blind to who's coming and going behind the virtual me.

James's Wife

I received a consult request for James reading "goals of care." On further research, the crux of the question at hand was *how* to care for him because he was declining evaluation and intervention for his coronary artery disease and arrythmia. He was in paroxysmal AFib, and his functional capacity had plummeted. He was also sixty-two, and from what his wife, Sharon, told me repeatedly, he was retired from the police force where he'd provided special forces training. She spoke of him grappling and besting men decades younger than him.

To initiate the consultation, I called the unit and got a bit of background from his nurse, Eric, about his status and the dynamics. Sharon was present and reviewing every medication and intervention, refusing most of them. James himself was polite but in some distress.

We began to set up the consult, and the camera cart was brought into the room.

On that particular day, the cart chose to be problematic. With most consults, there'd be some usually solvable technical challenge, but while the camera worked that day, the speaker didn't have incoming or outgoing sound.

Since we had a functional camera, I asked Eric to facilitate, using the phone to gather medical history, perform a review of systems, and dive into goals of care. James unfortunately didn't have the air for conversation, and the phone was passed to his wife, the gatekeeper. Sharon had never heard of palliative care, and therefore, she decided she didn't want the consult.

I could've pointed out that she wasn't my patient, and it wasn't her choice to refuse, but I knew better than to take that tactic and instead offered to hear his story and be an advocate if she was interested in the support. She again declined, but despite that, we were still talking some thirty minutes later. Because Eric had the cart in the room, I was able to see James while Sharon paced back and forth.

James's visage was quite concerning. Even though he looked five to ten years younger than his actual age and had a strong but lean structure to his body, he was using everything he had to the best of his ability simply to breathe. He was leaning forward on his bedside table in what we called the tripod position. It helped lift the rib cage and drop the diaphragm to make breathing easier. He clearly didn't have the air to insert himself into the conversation.

There were multiple questions at hand, and the clearest barrier to his care was Sharon's dangerous combination of medical literacy and distrust paired with her clear desire to be the voice of everything pertaining to him. If he wanted water, she had to check it first and ask questions about its source.

James had been on metoprolol and anticoagulants for his atrial fibrillation as an outpatient. The critical care team wanted to start him on an amiodarone drip and, due to a troponin spike and his known cardiac disease, send him to our larger hospital for a cardiac cath.

Sharon flatly refused amiodarone, stating, "I haven't heard of that drug, and I'm not putting him on anything unnatural that I haven't heard of."

The team was already at their wits' end, trying to provide education regarding medications, safety, and purpose. I wasn't the only one seeing his distress, and the team was clearly worried that he was decompensating.

Regarding cardiac catheterization, she flatly refused any invasive intervention. Her rationale was that he'd held black belts in martial arts and was stronger than men younger than him. She was essentially stating that *he* wouldn't want such interventions.

Code status was affirmed as full code, and I expressed my concerns that waiting until he suffered from cardiac arrest was a poor time to intervene. When I tried to ask him directly, she refused to pass the phone. When I asked Eric to ask him directly, she stood in front of the camera. The consult ended shortly after that without her accepting any plan to address his life-threatening concerns.

In the medium of telemedicine, I couldn't get close enough to speak with him directly or hold eye contact at his level.

Sometime after my attempted dialogue with James, his threatening sense of dyspnea became more acute. The ICU team got past Sharon and apparently didn't mince their words. The team worried that he might die, and James shared the concern at an infinitely more personal level—he wanted to be life flighted to the other hospital for help. They made arrangements and started amiodarone over the protestations of his wife. She had to be escorted from the unit.

In the end, the team was able to engage in person in ways I was unable to do remotely.

James and His Wife: Part Two

Interesting things began to happen when we gave James adequate oxygen and the opportunity to speak for himself. When I learned he'd been transferred to the hospital where I physically practiced, I reached out to the cardiac critical care team and asked that we be reconsulted for continuity of care. It turned out they were also becoming frustrated by the mixed messages and lack of clarity coming from his room.

My team was reconsulted.

Meeting with them both in person was a bit of déjà vu. Sharon wasn't expressing anger that he'd been transferred there; she merely continued her stories of James's past physical prowess. Her argument continued to be that *he* didn't want a cardiac catheterization or any new medications.

There was a moment of stunned shock when I finished one of her stories about James besting a younger officer in training on the mat.

"You've heard of him?!"

"Yes, Sharon. I heard a fair bit about him from you when we spoke yesterday."

"He wasn't here yesterday."

"We spoke on the phone and camera. I'm glad he's here, and it looks like he's breathing a bit better."

He *was* breathing better, but it was largely the result of supplemental oxygen and a far more livable heart rate—finally back below 140. He was lying back in bed and not in the tripod position. The question of cardiac catheterization still remained, along with consideration for cardiac ablation in the electrophysiology lab (EP) lab to better stabilize his aberrant rhythm. When I brought up the concerns regarding his diagnostic and interventional options, his wife promptly spoke up and asserted that he didn't want any of those things.

I calmly and respectfully pointed out, "I was asking your husband for his opinion and questions about his options."

Sharon responded with a tone of indignance. "I know what he wants! He doesn't want any of that!"

Despite James's past combat prowess, he didn't seem willing to grapple with his wife. I could see the will fade from his body. I prepared to expend the emotional energy to learn why she didn't want those things.

As other teams checked in while I was at the bedside, Sharon became distracted as she presented a laundry list of questions, complaints, and demands to the cardiology team. They took her seriously enough that she stayed focused on them. In most cases, like the coroner in an earlier story, it frustrated me when other teams arrived and interrupted the flow of the conversation. But it was a blessing that time.

I kneeled next to James and asked, "If you and I lose the ability to speak with each other, who would you want to make medical decisions for you?"

It might've been a watershed moment in his care. "Jessica. I want my daughter Jessie to make decisions, not her." He motioned to Sharon.

I told him I'd document that.

As the mass of the cardiology team approached the bedside to examine and speak with him, I took it as a cue to switch places and hear more of Sharon's stories. We spoke in the hall largely about things completely unrelated to James's immediate care.

While James was in his own space, he asked the cardiology team, "Can you make her go home?" He was finally finding the space to use his voice.

Sharon was politely asked to call it a day, and with less drama than we'd feared, she left. Later that day, James was able to tell the cardiology team that he wanted to go to the catheterization lab and see what they could do. Interventions were scheduled and followed through with. From that day on, the team made a point of asking Sharon to step out for examinations and the discussions that came with them. In the face-to-face setting, the integrity of James's voice could be honored simply because his wife was less able to speak over him.

The lesson I learned was that telemedicine lacks the subtle—but important—power of physical position and significantly shifted ownership of the conversation if someone had the ability and desire to dominate a patient.

James did well and walked out of the hospital following the stenting of a lesion and later ablation. I was so glad we got to help him find his voice.

Telemedicine Observations Before COVID-19

I just presented a case rich with the challenges and shortcomings of telemedicine in palliative care, but I don't wish to create the wrong impression because I'm still a strong proponent of using it to reach rural populations across distances to provide a service they may not otherwise have. The predominant experience involves effectively connecting with a patient or family at the bedside and doing the deep exploration of health threats and related goals of care. The reaction is often the expression of gratitude for taking the time to listen and discuss the difficult things.

The experience after the first few consults was far more familiar than different. In some ways, a telemedicine consult is exactly the same. In the setting of an intubated, encephalopathic, or dementia patient without family present, what follows is a phone conversation with the power of attorney, representative, or next of kin. This is the same whether the patient is twelve feet in front of me or 120 miles away.

Some of the challenges are the shift in power from patient to family in conversation, but this is arguably true in many in-person conversations as earlier stories observed. The biggest and most consistent challenges that I encountered in the first year were equipment availability or technical problems manifesting in a variety of frustrating ways.

On a recent busy morning, I attended a telemedicine consult for an ICU patient at one of our rural connected hospitals. I researched the patient electronically in hopes of doing a 9:30 a.m. consult. The rural hospital wasn't ready at that time, so we scheduled for 11:00

a.m. I paused preparation and drove to the nearby hospital and rounded on a few patients so I could be ready at 11:00 a.m., only to get a call that 11:00 a.m. would no longer work. Noon became the new time for a family meeting.

I called at noon only to learn that the family wasn't present. I considered videoing into the room so I could do my assessment but was told that the attending service also wanted to be present. It made sense to wait. The family finally arrived at 12:47. All that effort and prep took attention and mental energy, and I was more than ready to engage in the real work of the consult. The significant remaining problem was that the ICU's cart didn't work, and they didn't seem to know how to troubleshoot the problem or want to seek out an alternative. After a brief phone conversation with the patient's son, we elected to engage the following day at noon.

The next morning, I again reviewed the patient's status and prepared again, as a great deal could change in the ICU over the course of the night. I called the nurse and learned that some of the family were there. I decided to connect into the room and get started. Nothing had been addressed or fixed since the prior day, and the cart wouldn't work despite eighteen dial-in attempts. It was at that point that the nurse mentioned a power outage over the weekend and that the monitor was reading "not connected to service."

In telemedicine, you're reliant on the weakest link in the chain of communication. There's often some challenge, but with bilateral commitment to problem solving, we're almost always able to work past it. In that particular case, though, we failed that family and never did the consult.

During our young telemedicine service's first year, we completed approximately fifty-six consults at a single rural hospital. I traveled there, met staff, demonstrated an in-person consult, and broke the ice.

We started in the ICU, as we had a connection to the pulmonary critical care team rounding there. The flow of communication was also different in that the critical care doctor was serving as the consultant and not the attending. In my opinion, we did good work for the patients and families we met. The feedback from families, nursing, medical staff, and case managers also seemed to support this.

After the inaugural months, we slowly opened the service to the rest of the hospital. It's with a note of pride that I can say we began to fulfill an unmet need.

There's some irony in thinking how hard we had to work to convince people that this was a good idea. I had to prove there was a need and pushed back against institutional barriers for years. Somewhere over that time, things shifted to involve the strong support and engagement of other team members in building this program, and none of this could work without a team. We looked to open a service at a second rural hospital but didn't have the staffing for a scheduled drive-up to meet and greet stakeholders. We canceled that meeting and dealt with the high consult volume with plans to reschedule. It was a bit heartbreaking to be so close to further opening access and falter. Then, COVID-19 arrived.

A Pandemic Arrives

The whole world of healthcare shifted at a pace I'd never seen in my life. Suddenly, our morning conference was held via bridge line, and we restructured to decide which team members needed to be in the building. There was a lull in our record-setting volume as all elective admission, surgeries, and non-essential hospital stays halted. We went from fifty-eight inpatients at three hospitals all the way down to fifteen. Family visitation stopped, and we adjusted to a very different approach to our work.

Gradually, over the next three weeks, our volume skyrocketed. At one point, we had 380 percent of the volume of consults we were used to. It was around then that it was announced that our two remaining rural hospitals needed palliative care support. I asked my program director when we'd start thinking back to the laborious steps taken to previously launch the program.

"Monday. We'll be starting Monday."

It took us only two months to engage in as many virtual consults at the two additional hospitals as we had in the prior eleven months at the first hospital.

I could spend a portion of this book writing about the impact of the COVID-19 pandemic on my practice and my life. Sadly, I'm writing this portion of this book in late July 2020, and I'm under no illusion that we're anywhere near a definitive point in that story. I also have enough emotional self-awareness to know that I don't have the bandwidth to write this now. So far, I've seen more horrific deaths than I care to recall. I've been deeply connected to multiple families for multiple months, watching people who were healthy and did everything right. Some survived, and some died. I've seen colleagues both recover and die at ages younger than me. The saddest and most frequent themes are when spouses arrive together with COVID, and recovering children suffer while watching them remotely. More often than I'd like to recall, they don't always leave together; some don't leave at all. I'll revisit this portion of the book at a later point in time.

COVID-19 Pandemic

The pandemic that defined 2020 came into our collective consciousness with the quiet steps of a distant, abstract predator. It's easy for me to understand how many of us couldn't begin to appreciate the threat as real and formidable when it began to take hold. If you don't work in a hospital or see the stricken, the sun comes up and sets with the unaffected indifferences that match the normalcy of life. But in the early stages of 2020, the threat was abstract, even for those of us in this field.

As the first cases arrived in the United States and hit the news, a cold reality began to set in for those of us working in hospitals. We weren't unfamiliar with preparation for an abstract threat—one hospital in my network even has a unit dubbed the "Ebola unit."

COVID arrived as a sprinkling of cases met by an administration that had put aside the tools needed to stamp it out. Instead of being conscious of the lessons that history taught us from the 1918 Spanish flu pandemic, our national leadership took an active role in stripping society of its defenses by consistently denying or minimizing the threat, all while actively ridiculing state leaders who dared to protect their citizens. Instead of embracing the 80 percent effectiveness of wearing a mask as an act of patriotism, this simple step was marketed as an act of oppression.

The active undermining of state leadership gave license to citizens who were skeptical of wearing masks or social distancing. It metastasized into a political ideology later resulting in anti-mask crowds standing toe to toe with masked nurses in the streets of New York. In past generations, we mobilized a country for wars and were rich with national patriotism. In March of 2020, we had a former game show host at the helm who could've had China manufacture masks with his name instead of hats.

By November, most of America had seen past the lies and promises of a flu that would be gone by April, disappear with summer, or vanish after an election. It was no longer funny to think of our dear leader's past suggestions regarding ingesting bleach products or getting ultraviolet light inside the body. Seventy-seven people died taking elevated doses of hydroxychloroquine while the autoimmune population found access to chronic disease management meds needlessly threatened.[32]

I'd like to believe most of us wore masks in public and curtailed social visits. Outside of gas stations, a farm store, a pet store, and Ace Hardware, I hadn't been in a business to see. I didn't wish to test my public restraint at that point. America's resilience to do what were initially simple preventative measures had been largely burnt out.

As the pandemic began to take hold in the spring of 2020, we restructured how we engaged palliative medicine consultations. The winter holidays came and went, again putting us in the thick of a national crisis. The hospitals where I practiced were largely vacant of visitors but brimming with patients. At different peaks in this pandemic, I saw six of my newly consulted COVID patients die within the short span of two working days. In the winter of 2020 and 2021, I witnessed units that were never ICUs be named as such. The brand new "largest ER in the state of Pennsylvania" was filled to capacity shortly after opening. I was proud to be part of a network with effective leadership and dedicated staff, but that same well-supported staff couldn't be cloned to work newly created beds or master ICU skills overnight. Endless resilience didn't appear to be a realistic thing to expect. In the course of a year, I lost coworkers to burnout and watched them leave high-acuity roles in critical care. I held the phone for family as other colleagues died in the beds they once brought patients to. Many of us tried walking tall with the understanding that there were cracks beneath the surface.

We no longer met for team rounds in the morning but instead connected virtually before spreading out to various hospitals. Our

---

[32] K. Swank et al., "PDF," May 19, 2020.

small hospital office, known as "the closet," was too small for social distancing beyond three people. Our group lunches ended. Our counselor and social worker joined phone conversations from home, as did Michelle, our nurse who managed workflow logistics. The dark humor, sarcasm, and deep coping skills proved to fail miserably when we were in isolation dealing with the horrors wrought by the pandemic. After one of those early days, I pulled out of the back lot at the hospital and caught sight of a row of handwritten poster-board signs, each thanking front line and healthcare workers in a different way. I don't cry often.

In that same week, I picked up food from a local pizza shop for what would become the last time in months. I watched an obese middle-aged man in a yellow "don't tread on me" shirt with his bare face pick up his order. I looked at him with the expectation of seeing him again. He seemed like the archetype of so many of the patients who were dying in our ICUs.

Farther down the road, I pulled into a beer distributer and relaxed when I saw a No Mask No Service sign. Patrons were being served without having to enter by placing an order at the door. However, nobody inside wore a mask. I didn't return for eight months. I stopped entering any business with a semblance of busy about it. This was in part prudent and in part recognition that I feared my own anger if I encountered anyone vocally flaunting their lack of patriotism or care for others.

A Change in Care

The pandemic has changed how we engage palliative consultations in a multitude of ways. By curtailing visitation in the hospital to reduce spread, we also eliminated face-to-face family meetings. While I physically see all of my patients and talk by the bedside to those who can speak, those who love them most no longer have that luxury. This is both necessarily protective and equally brutal. I'm not advocating for open doors, but I have observed that isolation kills.

Ruth

Ruth was eighty-seven and had been a vibrant woman into her late seventies. Her family was close, and multiple generations still engaged with her regularly. Ruth had spent thirty years working first as a nurse in New York and then in Pennsylvania. The last twenty years of that career included work in a local nursing home. She began to develop symptoms of Alzheimer's dementia in the years that followed her eightieth birthday.

As her dementia progressed, she faced some of the common challenges, including wandering and confusion. She managed well at home until her husband died. The schedule and normalcy of home life crumbled without him as the anchor that held it all together. The family quickly began to realize how necessary that mutual support had been and how ill-equipped they were to provide the kind of structure she needed. Even so, she was early enough in the stages that she was able to request to go to the nursing home where she'd worked for the last two decades of her career.

Ruth thrived in the memory care unit. Her family had a wonderful balance of staggering their visits multiple times a week as children and grandchildren continued to see her.

It was not an uncommon sight to visit and find Ruth sitting behind the nurse's station, thumbing through charts. There were days when she felt she was at work, and the staff kindly supported whatever made her feel at home. Her family brought food and encouraged her to keep eating and, despite her memory loss, kept her engaged.

That picture of support, connection, and affirmation began to quickly crumble as COVID arrived. Ruth's nursing home was lucky in the sense that it was one of the few that didn't have an uncontrolled COVID outbreak. That might be due to the staff's willingness to follow guidelines, to restrictions on nearly all visitation, or to the end of communal meals or activities. Those steps were effective in keeping COVID out of Ruth—but came with the cost of isolation.

Ruth began to lose weight and stopped getting out of bed. She was having periods of agitation and could no longer attend to phone calls from a family struggling to keep her connected. She didn't have the ability to comprehend where her loving people had gone. With loss of appetite, she had a series of admissions for dehydration and acute kidney injury. Those temporary stays dealt with fixable short-term problems while also representing a downward spiral perhaps accelerated by her growing sense of isolation. What was there for Ruth to live for? Her family was wracked with a sense of guilt over circumstances they couldn't control.

COVID didn't ultimately kill Ruth, but it did play a role.

Seeing Is Believing

I was doing rounds on some of my ventilated COVID patients in the medical ICU when I was approached by one of our pulmonary critical care attending physicians.

"Craig, I have two patients who I want you to see, but I want to tell you about them before I put the consult order in. I think it's better if one person sees both of them."

That was my initial introduction to sixty-two-year-old Anselmo and sixty-seven-year-old Cecelio Marin. It was neither the first nor the last time we had family members on the same unit. The Marin brothers both had COVID-19 and were both in some trouble. Their children and Cecelio's spouse also had COVID but managed to avoid hospitalization. They were in disbelief at how the two brothers struggled.

Both of the Marin brothers had presented to the ER with complaints of fever and difficulty breathing, and at the time of consultation, they'd been hospitalized for less than a week. Cecelio had been seen the week prior and was tested for and diagnosed with COVID. He'd returned home with steroids and supplemental oxygen but needed to come back to the hospital when his breathing worsened. On the day of his return, he was supported on high-flow oxygen, but it quickly became apparent that he needed more. He was intubated and went to the ICU for additional ventilator support.

Anselmo came to the emergency department two days after his brother, telling the staff he had COVID. He was a model patient in many ways, but it was clearest in the way he tolerated oxygen and followed the guidance to lay prone in attempts to drain increasing pulmonary secretions. Three days following his admission, his oxygen needs continued to escalate. They transitioned him to the ICU—to a room almost across from his brother's.

I saw Cecelio first as I knew the bedside evaluation would be a briefer span of time because he was intubated and sedated. The real work in seeing him would be the following conversations with his family.

Cecelio was a robust man, and he was clearly critically ill. He was facedown on his belly with his head tilted to the side and his endotracheal tube positioned to keep it functional. He was so compromised that in addition to sedation, he needed to be completely restricted from body movement through the use of paralyzing drugs. He was in septic shock from COVID pneumonia, necessitating three separate IV drugs to keep his blood pressure up. In addition to these drugs, he also received volumes of IV fluid to help add fluid pressure to his lax blood vessels. Those numbers were holding. His oxygen level was a bit more tenuous and necessitated 100 percent oxygen. The remaining tools in the critical care toolbox were looking sparse if things worsened.

I called his spouse, Dolores, but it was their daughter, Marta, who answered. It turned out that Marta had become the spokesperson on this side of the family in part because Dolores spoke Spanish. I provided an overview of who I was and the role of a palliative care team. In a few minutes, I also learned that her brother, Antonio, and Dolores's sister were also in the room. The younger half of the audience spoke English while the older half hailed from the Dominican Republic and spoke Spanish. Legally speaking, Dolores was the decision-maker of the family while Marta was acting as the spokesperson. Culturally, within this family it was unclear if some of this authority had been delegated due to language differences. Within a few minutes of conversation, I convinced Marta that it would be best to take some of the translation burden off her shoulders and call back with a translator.

I called our translation service and provided the medical record number as part of the process. I often worried about the trauma some translators endured as they were suddenly placed in the middle of difficult conversations without any context or follow-up. The conversations were emotional, and on more than one occasion, I'd seen a translator tear up as they formed a bridge with a family in crisis. Knowing it might be difficult, I took a moment to explain that we'd be discussing Cecelio's critically ill status with extended family.

We connected the call, and Marta was able to put me on speaker phone with the present family members. There was also the chatter of younger voices, a portion of eight grandchildren in the background. We began to discuss from head to toe what Cecelio was in the midst of. Visualizing and understanding the use of a ventilator took some work as Dolores would intermittently ask if she could speak with Cecelio—someone who was not only intubated but also facedown, sedated, and paralyzed.

Cecelio was only about five days into his ventilator course at that stage. The conversation was mostly about supporting the family, helping them understand, and establishing a framework for future decisions that they might need to navigate. The first sizable goals of care questions had been answered earlier. He was intubated. Renal function had deteriorated with the progressive deepening of shock, and prior to his current positioning, the team had discussed the need for dialysis. He had access placed for continuous renal replacement therapy. The timing had proved to be critical, as he had become too unstable to tolerate rotation to a supine position, which would've rendered dialysis access placement untenable.

The family's collective answer had effectively been that they trusted us to do what was needed to keep Cecelio alive. The lack of visitation meant that so much of his health status was lost in translation. I could see an overweight, critically ill man on dialysis, ventilation, three pressors, insulin, bicarb, propofol, fentanyl, cisatracurium, and IVF. His nine IV drips created a spaghetti of lines that were taped to the floor and run under the sliding glass door to the hallway. This was an ingenious trick nursing had developed to manage the unending task of changing out IV infusions from outside a high-risk environment, but it also further contributed to an image of an isolated man lying at the convergence of extensive medical equipment.

All his family could envision was a gregarious father/spouse/brother-in-law who was walking around two weeks ago.

Code status was affirmed as full code. I began to set the stage for future consideration of long-term ventilator support with a tracheostomy and a feeding tube. At day five on the vent, this option would be weeks away, but it was also pretty clear that the depth of his illness ensured we would get to this decision—if he survived that long. The answer was yes but followed by the disconnect of asking when he could come home. The family tried to assure me they understood he was really sick, followed by statements that they could take care of him at home. Over the course of the thirty-minute conversation, it became clear that there was much the family couldn't understand and that the focus on aggressive care would likely remain unchanged even with full comprehension. I knew in the coming days that I'd have to meet with them again and set up a video call in the room to help them grasp the evolving reality. At the end of the call, I told them I'd be seeing Anselmo next and follow up intermittently.

Anselmo was five years younger than his brother and probably weighed a good fifty pounds less. Outside of some high blood pressure, his medical history was relatively benign. His chest x-ray showed bilateral opacities, and his effort to breathe corroborated this. He was seated upright in bed with an Optiflow™ cannula in place, giving him fifty liters per minute of 100 percent oxygen. In the months preceding his admission, we learned that being as aggressive as possible in avoiding intubation conferred a higher likelihood of survival. In reality, the ICU teams had come up with additional ways to move the boundary for intubation a bit further back, but Anselmo was sitting on the razor-thin edge of needing it. In addition to his Optiflow™, steroids, remdesivir, and antibiotics, he had an added second source of oxygen via a mask.

English wasn't Anselmo's first language, but he spoke it well enough for us to have a focused conversation. It needed to work because an iPad translator would be unlikely to be heard over the volume of noise from his oxygen, and no in-person translator would or should join me in the room with the COVID virus being jettisoned throughout the air.

I shared that I was going to try to spare his energy by being more direct with my discussion. I said, "Right now, we are really worried about your breathing."

He nodded back, but I was left with the sense that I was more worried than he was at that stage. What amazed me on more than one occasion was how someone could be struggling to breathe and not appear to understand how much danger they were in.

"We're worried that your body may tire out and you wouldn't be able to breathe on your own. If that happens, we may need to insert a breathing tube." I needed to elaborate further as he seemed only to be listening and not responding or reacting. "If we need to do that to keep you alive, should we?"

"Yes," he said.

It was his fatigued shrug that seemed to say, "Duh, why wouldn't you keep me alive?"

I affirmed that we would continue to try to avoid a breathing machine, but we'd have one take over if needed. The answer to CPR was a similar indifferent shrug. The disconnect became more apparent when I took the ventilator question a step forward.

"If we have to use a ventilator, we always try to get someone off of it as soon as we can. Sometimes, though, we're unable to do so and have to make decisions about whether or not to make it permanent. We do this by placing a tracheostomy in the neck and a feeding tube in the belly. If we can't get you off of a ventilator, should we ever do that?"

Anselmo asked, "Will I still be able to work with that?"

Anselmo had worked as a limo driver, possibly contributing to his COVID exposure. I explained that long-term ventilators would mean time in a nursing home. He clarified that we could use a ventilator, but he was unable to make decisions about long-term or permanent ventilation. His oxygen saturation was hovering in the mid-eighties, and I was taking a portion of the fading reserve that he desperately needed. We closed the conversation by clarifying who should make decisions for him if he became too short of breath to talk.

Anselmo named his children as his representatives. Families were often amorphic in nature, and it took some time to reconcile names on the chart with the reality of his sizable family. He had a son, Angel, in Pennsylvania and a daughter, Elena, farther north in the state. The woman listed, Alejandra, proved not to be his wife but a girlfriend—later learned to be the mother of both Angel and Elena.

The name Ruben was on the chart, but he was her son and not Anselmo's. To complicate things further, Anselmo had other children in the Dominican Republic and possibly even a wife. In total, there were seven different names listed. After speaking with Elena, I learned that Anselmo wasn't just a driver but a mechanic and family legend. He had financially supported the children of multiple cousins in the Dominican Republic, helping them gain citizenship and work in NYC and Hazelton over the decades. He was viewed as a savior in his family and community for the way he was perceived as rescuing relations. Suddenly, it made sense that the question Anselmo was most focused on was whether or not he'd be able to work with a ventilator.

The week that followed for each of the brothers was not good. Cecelio continued to need high-flow ventilation support but was finally able to tolerate being rotated faceup. He had considerable facial edema and some skin breakdown from the days he spent prone. COVID often kept on giving, but not in a good way. For Cecelio, this manifested as a pneumothorax. His lung ruptured under the strain of ventilator support and the tissue rigidity induced by concentrated oxygen. He received a chest tube and remained about as critically ill as one could.

The ICU continued to update the family. I made a series of calls during that week but kept missing them. His children were at work, and his spouse didn't answer. I suspected the language barrier contributed to that. Even so, his children were diligent in checking up in the evenings, and I could read about the "family update calls."

For three days, Anselmo managed to get by with oxygen support. Each day, when I'd check his chart or look in through the glass ICU doors, I was impressed to see him breathing with only a moderate amount of work and no ventilator. I checked in with Elena after she left a message and assured her that we were continuing support. She still carried the weight of updating multiple people. The goals were clear, and at that stage in the hospital course, it was a matter of full support and observing the clinical evolution of his story.

On the evening of the fourth day, COVID threw one of its devastating curve balls. That foul pitch came in the form of a large MCA territory stroke. His speech slurred, and he slumped to an immobile right side. He was intubated both for respiratory distress and the inability to adequately protect his airway from his own secretions. The ICU team alerted Elena during the night, and I arrived the next day to learn the news.

For Anselmo, the stroke was like a tipping domino that cascaded into increased critical care needs. His pulmonary status deteriorated further after ventilator support, and he also entered into a shock state requiring pressors. As if COVID and a stroke weren't enough, the hypercoagulable state that COVID might induce contributed to the development of critical limb ischemia. Vascular surgery became involved in an emergent consultation, and he was taken to the operating room for limb salvation thrombectomy. Ironically, this was on his functional side. Elena had been receiving updates with each twist in his story, and consent for each intervention occurred rapidly.

Two to three weeks into Cecelio's ICU course, he continued to dance a close tango with death. Communication with family was critical but not always easy. As team members, we understood each other fairly well. The challenge came with variation in language, especially a second language. We could say the same thing to a team member as to a family member, and the result would be wildly different understandings.

Cecelio's need for pressors had come down from three agents to one. His oxygen needs had reduced from 100 percent to 80 percent. His family was ecstatic that he was making a recovery. Somehow, the idea that he remained on dialysis and high-flow oxygen and was paralyzed, sedated, and in line for permanent ventilation and artificial nutrition was being glossed over with the polish of undying optimism.

Optimism could be an appropriate survival mechanism. Most of us could look back at events in our own lives and see things we wouldn't have overcome or endured were it not for optimism. I tried not to take that from people, as I too liked to hope and believe in miracles. But miracles were rare by nature, and optimism was a balance that rested on the fulcrum of truth with the larger reality weighing down the opposite side.

It came as a bit of a shock when I reached Marta to discuss his status and some of the decision points at hand. He was now twenty-one days on the ventilator, and we were past the point where we would historically make a transition to tracheostomy and PEG tube or the starkly different pathway of comfort care. Cecelio's body had made some small positive moves regarding his level of support. The team's perceptions of this versus the family's were worlds apart. He was too unstable with his oxygen needs to be able to safely undergo the procedure for placement of a tracheostomy. I often reminded families when they asked about the surgical risk of tracheostomy placement that by its very nature, it was a procedure we only needed to perform on the critically ill. To be too critically ill for a tracheostomy actually said a great deal about one's health status. He clearly had a long-term need for ventilator support with a poor overall prognosis, even if we could get to that step.

But Marta remained puzzled, saying, "He's doing better. Do we need to do that?"

I took time to explain the valuable but—in the big picture—small changes in her father's state. I talked about the rigid nature of his lungs and the difficulty he was having in using them to absorb oxygen. I tried to convey that this difficulty would mean long-term, potentially permanent, need for ventilator support. His picture was further compounded by renal failure and the extended nature of his acute illness. She began to understand his prognosis a bit more deeply. I didn't ask her to answer the question of a tracheostomy, partially because it would be her mother's decision, but also because no action would be taken that day. I did, however, recommend further family discussion.

Three weeks into the hospital stay, Anselmo's prognosis was looking worse instead of better. Much like his brother, we were approaching a decision point about tracheostomy and PEG tube placement. He was also too unstable to proceed with the actual surgical procedure, but at least his lung compliance and imaging appeared better than his older brother.

In back-and-forth conversations with Angel and Elena, we explored what the family believed Anselmo found to be important in life. Clear themes in these conversations were always paired closely with his ability to work. When we explored those themes as it related to his yet to be fully defined functional deficits, it remained unclear from the family's perspective what Anselmo would want us to do. Elena wasn't confident about moving toward a tracheostomy and potential life in a nursing home requiring custodial care. Angel was taking a fighter in a battle position at a conceptual level. A summarizing statement would be, "Dad fought for us, so we should fight for him. He'll fight this." They diverged in their bias, though no formal decision about tracheostomy or PEG tube was reached in that round of discussions. Code status, however, was answered after multiple days and some independent family exploration. If his body decided for him and death arrived, then they would respect that and not ask for CPR. All other supports were fully engaged.

Four and five weeks into his hospital stay, Cecelio was no closer to leaving the ICU and was, in fact, further away from the potential transitional step of tracheostomy and PEG tube placement. It's worth noting that the length of an ICU stay is considered a prognostic indicator with the median time being just shy of four days, and Cecelio had been there for over thirty-five. [33] His oxygen requirements hadn't improved, and he presented a new picture of sepsis and bacteraemia. He was again resting in a prone position and unable to tolerate being flipped onto his back due to his oxygenation status. Not only was he too unstable, but his neck was also inaccessible.

His family became more comfortable in maintaining a position of optimism in favor of ongoing aggressive support. They couldn't see the full picture. I don't feel that we can fully expect a family to really see or conceptualize a health status when they can't physically see their loved one. It was harder to understand a verbal description of physical endurance and discomfort than it was to see it with one's own eyes. Our medical words were as much a foreign language to this man's children as English was to his spouse. Visitation policies that were designed to minimize exposure to COVID by reducing visitor traffic also crippled decision-making. As it related to the ICU, visitors were only allowed for the actively dying or those transitioning off life support.

On a Friday evening, the pulmonary critical care team added additional pressors to treat his worsening shock. His arterial blood gasses showed deepening acidosis. Cecelio was dying. His family

---

[33] Jack E. Zimmerman et al., "Intensive Care Unit Length of Stay: Benchmarking Based on Acute Physiology and Chronic Health Evaluation (APACHE) IV," *Critical Care Medicine* 34, no. 10 (2006): 2517-2529, https://doi.org/10.1097/01.ccm.0000240233.01711.d9

was called in to pay respects. In medical care, we were not obligated to offer medical care that was deemed to be futile. After seeing him in person, Cecelio's family was told that we would not perform CPR when his heart stopped. There was a consensus documented by multiple physicians that this would be futile. The family, having seen him in person, recognized the accuracy of the statement and accepted it. I wasn't part of this dialogue but came to understand they appreciated that moment of paternalism in not being asked to decide anything. The family went home Friday night with a different understanding of the magnitude of his illness. Cecelio died Saturday afternoon.

Anselmo remained across the hall without any improvement in his clinical status. I never figured out if he was aware his brother had been roughly fifty feet away for the past month. I remember talking to him about his options and trying to explain what a ventilator was before his stroke. Even in his distressed state, he'd been polite and tried to follow the information I presented. I felt like I failed him while being asked to make my best attempt in the worst of times.

As his clinical status deteriorated and his kidneys began to fail, his children were also called in to visit. This time, they were offered a chance to see him before we talked about access for and initiation of dialysis. Their ability to make decisions might've been tempered by the larger family's experience with their uncle's hospital course. After seeing him, the options of adding dialysis or abstaining from adding additional interventions versus outright stopping critical care support were presented. Both Elena and Angel struggled with the idea of stopping. They were able, at that stage, to articulate that their dad wouldn't find life in a nursing home while paralyzed and ventilated to be acceptable. They just couldn't act on that and instead chose a middle ground of not adding dialysis or second and third agents for hypotension. They, or at least Angel, articulated a need to feel like they fought. I assured them that they'd advocated that idea, and he fought. I knew they struggled on his behalf out of love, and I wished we were having a different conversation and that their father had a different prognosis. They were allowed to visit at that time because both the team and the family were acknowledging death was coming. Anselmo became anuric and died four days after that discussion. These consults were usually not a process of limited visits and quick decision-making but more often a long relationship by acute care standards.

The Darkest Week

April 2020

As I write this chapter, it's spring, 2020. During this pandemic, I've had the good fortune of working with a phenomenal team within a larger organization with effective leadership. Despite these invaluable positives, I've witnessed some network colleagues or their family members dying. Some of these people were a decade younger than me. I've also heard many nurses and critical care providers speak to me or to others and say that they've had too much, resulting in some completely leaving while others break down. These are incredibly emotionally strong and intelligent people.

The most difficult portion of this past year has been the periods of isolation while at work. So far, COVID has presented in two sizable waves of volume and acuity, and during the first one, I found myself as the sole provider from my team at the smaller hospital where we consult. The ICU, before it expanded, consisted of approximately eighteen beds. Over the course of a weekend, I was consulted on 50 percent of the ICU patients. The consult requests would typically read "goals of care" and have a brief status biopic for the patient. That weekend, it included things like COVID-vent day X, COVID-renal failure, COVID-trach/PEG discussion, COVID-incidental finding of renal cell carcinoma, alcoholic cirrhosis-COVID, advanced dementia-COVID. I hope for those of you who have read this far that there's an understanding that the work of clarifying goals of care requires a deep dive and a certain reserve of emotional energy. Most of the conversations included discussions with multiple family members. Interspersed with those discussions were periods of gowning and gearing so families could visually see the patient on video. Few others had the time to do this in the fast pace of critical care. Nobody from my team was coming in on the weekend or joining me during the week. It wasn't neglect or malice but simply reflected the volume of work across the system. Everyone was working exceptionally hard.

I sat in the waiting room that was supposed to be vacated of visitors to try to chart and eat between consults. The ICU nurses had acquired the unenviable role of communicating and frequently enforcing the no visitation policy. One particular family would drive ninety minutes each day and call this patient's nurse from the parking lot for an update. Each day, they'd attempt to visit. And like so many other visitors, they were barred from an ICU rife with COVID. We wanted to protect that son, that husband, and all the others they'd interact with.

The elderly husband spoke the same dialect of his wife of sixty years. He'd been allowed to visit earlier in her hospital course, as there were no appropriate translation resources. That, of course, changed when she was intubated and unconscious. But it did not change her husband's resolve to visit or her son's willingness to drive him down. Each day, they'd attempt and often succeed in making it to the second floor, pulling the nurse away from patient care to reiterate the same things she had just told him on the phone.

"No, sir, you can't visit. Yes, sir, I'll tell her you were here." She wouldn't be aware. "Yes, I know you want to see her. Yes, I know you've been married for sixty years."

The exchange was a circular conversation that lasted for a very, very, very long ten minutes. The patient's son negotiated in a different way. I could hear both the heartbreak in the nurse's voice as well as the anger being chained down with her professional responses. The nurse again reiterated the visitation policy and the rationale behind it.

"You can call. You can come to the parking lot if you need to. You can call from anywhere. Every minute you have me out here means I'm not in there taking care of her. Please don't make me turn you away every day."

I'd been sitting there ready to engage and back her up if I needed to, but I was afraid an additional entry into the conversation would only muddy or prolong the discussion. She knew I was watching, as it was the only thing happening in the large room. The old man with his cane wiped the tears from his cheek and finally walked across the room to the door with his son. She stood there until they rounded the corner and then slumped into a chair.

"Every day, I have to make that old man cry. People ask me how I'm doing, and I used to say day by day. Now it's hour by hour. That all I've got." The tears rolled silently down her face, being absorbed by her mask. She stood up, turned, and went back into the unit. It was only noon. She had many more hours to go.

I would go home and try not to hear the frustrations of my children dealing with remote learning. I watched the news and heard the administration speaking of how the "China virus" wasn't so bad and would be gone by summer. We cancelled our summer vacation, knowing the patently obvious. I listened to citizens struggle to rub together two synapses in misguided attempts to form a cogent thought about why masks were bad. One woman ranted in a state hearing about her freedom to not wear masks and went as far as to shout that she wasn't wearing underwear because her vagina needed to breathe. I think more than her vagina had had an anoxic insult at some point.

Back at work over the course of two days, six of those patients who I'd been consulted on died. I was the link for many of those families along with the nurses for those who could visit. With each family and patient group there was the task of removing drips and equipment that had become more death's delay than life support. It was a heavy emotional toll on an empty tank driving along in an angry and divided nation. I pulled out of the hospital that day with more of a mix of rage than despair. As I sat at the light to leave the hospital, a song came the radio, providing the dark inappropriate release that I needed: Queen's "Another One Bites the Dust." I turned up the radio to full blast, rolled down all four windows, opened the sun roof, and shouted along without a flying fuck!

It was with every shred of conscious reserve that I resisted the urge to turn off traction control and unleash burnt rubber at full throttle into a smoking arc when the light changed.

I made it home that day too spent to do the things I usually did to recharge my batteries. I fed the kids and was in bed by 8:15 with my scrubs out for the next day.

The death count continued to rise. In the following months, I learned when I could afford to watch the news. I have the huge blessing of owning a basement gym and equipment that's served me since high school. I took my anger out on forged iron and chased after college personal best weight-lifting records.

The Long Conversation

Most healthcare relationships draw strength and trust from how well you build them. This is often critical in the work of palliative consultation. In most of my inpatient consults, I'm meeting that patient and family for the first time. This means we're often doing the work of building a new relationship in a time of considerable stress. This final patient story takes place in a time of family stress, unknowns, fears, and distance.

Robert Smithington was sixty-three and presented to the hospital ER in early October with a complaint of a cough and fever. He received some antibiotics for pneumonia and some steroids to help open his airways. His chest x-ray was concerning, showing pneumonia affecting both lungs, and a COVID-19 test was pending. He was well enough that he didn't need supplemental oxygen, and he was discharged from the emergency department with prescriptions for antibiotics and steroids.

The clinical suspicion for COVID-19 infection proved accurate as the test results returned positive the following day. Robert had attempted going back to work, but after a day, returned home to try to recover and rest. In the course of that week, his breathing worsened, and he went from telling his wife he didn't need to go back to the hospital to asking that he take her. Sue didn't waste time and loaded him into their pickup and got him there.

That time, Robert needed to be admitted for oxygen support, antibiotics, and the antiviral drug, Remdesivir. Visitation policies were being enforced with the community prevalence of COVID elevated. They said goodbye to each other in the emergency department, and Sue went home. In the days that followed, Robert seemed to be the model patient. He made the attempts to lay prone in hopes of draining pulmonary secretions. Sue and their sons would intermittently text him back and forth.

Robert didn't have the good fortune of improving in that first week, and his oxygen requirements began to escalate. He was soon on 100 percent oxygen at fifty liters per minute through an Optiflow[tm] set up. He tolerated the high-flow oxygen for about three days, then his body crumpled in fatigue. An endotracheal tube was inserted to allow a ventilator to take over the breathing for him. The ICU team had taken the time to ask him in advance if that step would be okay, and he had agreed.

With the addition of the ventilator, an oral-gastric feeding tube was placed as a temporary means. Robert really hadn't been eating well the week prior to hospitalization, and he didn't have the air to spare for eating in the days before being intubated. His body went into shock caused by the sepsis from his pneumonia. In the small community hospital, he quickly became one of the sickest patients in the ICU. The team made the assessment that his best chance for survival was a transfer to a larger hospital.

Once he arrived in his new ICU room, his care continued. He required 70 percent oxygen and prone positioning. He was now in deepening shock, and a second IV agent was added to help maintain his blood pressure. His family received sporadic updates following the transfer and struggled to translate the medical language of differing providers. "This value is going up; this value is going down; he's stable; he's critically ill; his oxygen numbers are good, but he's acidotic." He was also fifty miles from home, and his family had not seen him in over a week.

Palliative medicine was consulted seven days after the transfer with a request that read, "Goals of care, COVID, COPD, poor prognosis." I received the consult and spent my time reviewing the chart before walking over to the ICU to see him and speak directly with the team members. They were concerned that his family was having difficulty understanding his status and needed some support in making decisions. He'd been requiring ventilator support for eight days and was stable but critically ill. His peak and plateau pressures on the ventilator were consistently high. In a nutshell, Robert wasn't making progress, and his lungs were becoming stiff. He wasn't in a position to wean off ventilation in the near future.

I called Sue and received an answer from another woman before the phone was passed over, hearing some rustled commotion followed by the tension in Sue's voice. I initiated the conversation by stating where I was calling from, my name, and that I wasn't calling with any new news, good or bad. She thanked me for that quick clarification, and some of the pressure went down a notch.

"I was consulted to see your husband and try to be of support to you and your family. I'm part of the palliative medicine service, and my role is to help families navigate complex health situations and sometimes make decisions." I shared that I'd spoken with the critical care team and taken some time to read through her husband's chart. "It wasn't a short read; your husband has a lot going on. But the things that aren't usually in the chart are some of the things that tell me who he is as a person. I'm hoping you can help fill in some of those blanks. Before COVID and this hospital stay, how was your husband doing?"

Sue told me he was short of breath the week before he came to the ER the first time.

I responded, "I know, but how was he doing a month ago or a year ago?"

The conversation continued to unfold, and we took natural segues to talk about Robert as a person. I learned that he was a long-haul truck driver for his entire adult life. Sue had often traveled with him to see the country when they were younger. Together, they'd raised four sons, and two had joined him in the trucking industry. It seemed they grew up under his tutelage behind the wheel as well.

Their four sons were married, and most had two or three young children. Extended family, despite an affinity for the open road, mostly stayed close in their hometown. There were multiple cousins and their families who frequently checked in with Sue for updates.

"Tell me, what are the things Robert does for fun? What puts a smile on his face?"

I wasn't surprised to hear that family was a big part of his life. His granddaughter's softball games and hunting trips were a large feature. Barbeques and social gatherings were what made him happy. It seemed he couldn't go out for a pack of cigarettes without running into somebody and losing an hour in conversation. It was good to just talk about Robert without touching on anything medical, but it soon became time to pull the conversation back into the ICU.

"Can you tell me what you've been hearing from the team about your husband's health?"

Sue gave back pieces of information that assembled into a frame of understanding. She could tell me that he wasn't breathing on his own and was having trouble with his blood pressure. She relayed some of the words that had been used but which seemed to contradict, such as stable and critically ill, and she didn't understand the relationship between shock and blood pressure and asked for clarification on whether it was high or low. To her, shock meant something electrical.

I asked if she wanted me to try to fill in some of the informational gaps. She was interested but paused to ask if her cousin, Paula, could be part of the conversation. Paula was the person who originally answered the phone and happened to be a nurse's aide. I welcomed the opportunity and supported her by observing that sometimes an extra set of ears was really useful. It was also good to have a second person coming up with questions.

With both on the phone, I indicated that I'd give a head-to-toe rundown on Robert's health status. I learned from the earlier conversation that Sue seemed to process broader information better and was less interested in granular detail. I said I would share what was going well but also what things we worried about. Peak pressures, blood gas values, drug names, and lab values would only be a part of the conversation if they took it to those focal points.

I shared that he was sedated so he'd be more relaxed and allow the ventilator to take charge of breathing. I told them that sometimes we actually used drugs to completely paralyze the body in order to reduce oxygen demand but were not currently doing that with him. I brought up that COVID had damaged his lungs, and we were trying to reduce inflammation and also treating for bacterial pneumonia as well.

"The body's response to infection is often a drop in blood pressure. This is the shock we talked about earlier. We're giving him drugs to tighten up his blood vessels and fluid to raise his pressure high enough to support organ function. The stable part is that we've been holding steady on these drugs as well as the ventilator support. The critically ill part is that he continues to need all this. Stable, in his case, is both good and a worry. He's neither improved nor gotten worse in the past two days, but it's still a concern because we're not in a great spot. We've also been keeping a close eye on kidney function—they're working, but under some distress. If that gets worse, we'll talk about things like dialysis. He doesn't need that now, and we hope he won't."

It took them a while to ask follow-up questions, and I could hear the pieces of information clicking into some places. I acknowledged that it was a lot to process, kind of like getting information from a fire hose as opposed to a garden hose.

I said, "There are some things I'd like to put on your radar for the future. I want you to have some time to think before we have to make any decisions. We've been using the ventilator for about eight days. We always try to get someone off of the machine as soon as we find they can safely breathe on their own. Unfortunately, we're worried that we're pretty far away from that point with the way things look today. If things improve, we'll celebrate and move forward. If they stay the same or get worse, we may need to make decisions about whether or not to make the ventilator permanent or semi-permanent with a tracheostomy."

Sue asked, "What's that?"

Paula answered, "They make a hole in his neck, and he breathes through that."

I clarified further by saying that the machine would still breathe for him, but yes, through an attachment in his neck below the vocal cords. I explained that it was a step if people needed a longer period of time before coming off of a ventilator.

"When do we have to decide?" Sue asked.

I told her that we used to start thinking about it after two weeks, but with COVID, we'd been waiting longer. I also pointed out that he was sicker than we'd like for a procedure that, by nature, we only did on critically ill patients.

"We can talk about this more as his health status continues to change."

Sue agreed and added that she'd need to talk further with their sons before any decisions were made. She did express a bias by saying, "I'm not sure he would want that."

I didn't discuss the long-term care and needs that would follow. That would be a conversation for a different day depending on how his story evolved.

The conversation began to wind down, and I said, "I have one more question to ask, and it may be difficult to answer. It's also okay if you don't have an answer. Does Robert have a living will?"

"No."

"I'm going to ask you some of the questions that are on a living will in a hypothetical way. But I want to be clear first. We're not talking about stopping anything at this moment. We're continuing his drips; we're using the ventilator and going up on oxygen if we need to; we're doing tests; we're being medically vigilant and intervening when things change. With all of this still going on, if his heart stops on its own, we have two choices. One choice is to be medically aggressive and do CPR. We might get a heartbeat back, but it won't fix his lung problems. The other choice is to say that death is unfortunate but natural and not do CPR. If his body decides on its own, what would he want us to do?"

Sue's answer sounded both raw and honest. "I don't know. I don't know. I just don't know. Do what you can. Do the CPR thing."

I shared with her that that was the ICU team's current understanding, and I wouldn't change anything. We gradually de-escalated the emotions of the topic, and I moved toward a closing question and asked, "Is there anything I'm missing or you feel like we should be talking about?"

Sue had questions about visitation but quickly grasped the active policy restrictions. She then asked if I could speak with their son, Frank, and talk about what we talked about. It was in that moment I realized that we didn't have contact information for any of his kids. She gave me Frank and Gavin's phone numbers, and I passed on my office number. I told her she could also share the number with their sons, and I'd follow up with Frank later in the day. I thanked her for her time, and she thanked me back. We ended the call with a loose plan to follow up intermittently.

It had been a long conversation, and I needed a break. I wasn't surprised or put off by not having a list of decisions or goals. The short-term goals were to continue all critical care support. The long-term goals would have to evolve with his clinical course and her family's assimilation of complex medical language affecting someone they love dearly.

I called Frank but didn't reach him that day. I was honestly relieved to be leaving a message as I was running low on emotional energy, and my own bandwidth for a deep-dive conversation was low. I had a sense that this was going to be a consult spanning multiple days. Frank did return my call later in the day, and I received the message the next morning.

I called him back after seeing his father. Shortly after he answered, he asked if it would be okay if we connected with Gavin. The three of us spent time going over much of the same information that I reviewed the day before with their mother and Paula. We covered some knowledge gaps about pressors and lung compliance and touched on future decision-making points such as tracheostomy, a PEG tube, and code status. They expressed a bias in favor of each of those steps while also indicating it would ultimately be their mom's decision.

I also learned that Sue, Paula, Frank, some cousins, and a maternal uncle were all in various stages of recovering from COVID. Gavin hadn't been tested, but his wife had been struggling with her energy levels after her bout with the virus. COVID had a broad impact on their family, with Robert bearing the worst of it. They thanked me for my time, and I said I'd mostly check in with their mom on other days. From then on, I kept a pattern of checking the chart daily and rounding on him every other day.

About twenty-two days into his hospital stay, I had reason to make contact and take another deep dive with the family. I reached out to Sue, and we set up a time for a 3:00 p.m. phone conference with her, Gavin, Paula, pulmonary critical care, and Cathie, the social worker on my team. In the course of those three weeks, Robert had periods where his oxygen requirements were in the seventies and a brief two days where he was off pressors. On some of the better days, the question of tracheostomy had been raised again and agreed to only for him to again become too unstable to proceed. That day's call was about his deteriorating renal function and three necrotic toes on his right foot.

The family questions were insightful.

"If you can place dialysis access, why can't you do the tracheostomy?"

"How many times will he need it?"

"Why did this happen to his toes?"

"Is he going to get better from this?"

Each of their questions led the conversation down different pathways. There was uncertainty about his kidneys' potential to recover. His toes were compromised from prolonged vascular constriction from drugs to treat shock. The tracheostomy was more difficult because of his critically high needs for oxygen. The collective team was worried that he wouldn't recover from COVID. I shared that none of us could predict the future, but in a best-case scenario, we were looking at significant debility and prolonged institutionalization.

Sometimes, when families are overwhelmed, the capacity to make decisions crashes because we'd given them too much information. The Smithington family's decisional capacity was in a state of paralysis, and they negotiated for time. "Can we place the dialysis catheter and decide later?"

Together, we observed that doing one without a decision for the other wouldn't be logical, but while we strongly anticipated his need for dialysis, it wasn't imminent that day. We agreed that they could discuss independently and give us an answer the following day.

I rounded on Robert the next morning and then called Sue from outside the room. She shared that the family had discussed it, and they supported moving forward with dialysis. I let her know that I'd inform the team, and we'd likely take steps to start later that day. His kidney numbers had deteriorated overnight, but his critically ill picture was otherwise frustratingly stable. While I had her back on the phone, I took the time to revisit code status again. It had been two weeks since we'd last discussed it.

Her response indicated a direction but not a decision. "I'm not sure about doing that anymore, but I need to talk with the family. I need to see him first." I reminded her that nothing else would change our approach in his care if she and her family decided to change code status. I also acknowledged her desire to see him and offered an in-room video visit.

We disconnected the call while I geared up, and I reconnected with her from the anteroom. In some ways, it felt like the reverse of a telemedicine visit yet still different from walking in with a physical family member. On video, the attention was mostly where I directed the camera. In a physical visit, there was sometimes a discussion of the equipment and alarms. I found myself resisting the temptation to fall into the familiar of discussing the peripheral things and instead just let her see her husband.

With the focus of the camera on Robert's face, Sue asked questions about the things she could see. "Does the tube hurt? Can he feel it? Why is his face so puffy? Can he hear us?"

I answered, "He's sedated, partly with the narcotic fentanyl, so he might not be comfortable but shouldn't feel the tube as overt pain. His face is puffy from all the extra fluid we gave him and from the days he's spent lying facedown. It's edema. His ears work, but his ability to think and process anything like a conversation is blunted by the sedation he needs. It doesn't hurt to say the things you feel you need to say."

For the next few minutes, I just stopped talking and held the camera steady.

"I love you, Bertie. You better not quit on me. Rex and Tigger miss you and keep sitting in your chair. I love you." Sue did a commendable job of speaking through the cracks in her voice and managed to say that she loved him in ways that only two people who have spent decades together can. The ventilator intermittently interrupted her with high pressure alarms in the background. His nurse came in to suction him, and I used that as a reason to exit the room. We ended the call with an open-ended plan to follow up in the future.

The week ended, and I covered a different hospital the following week. I was too busy with the patients there to remotely check Robert's status. Fortunately, Cathie had made a connection and checked in with Sue, and dialysis started after access was placed. The week trudged on with him remaining critically ill and stable—twenty-nine days away from his family in a hospital far from home.

On day thirty-two, I rounded on him again. He was under continuous renal replacement therapy (CRRT), a form of around-the-clock dialysis we used when the body couldn't handle the fluid shifts of traditional dialysis. The past week had been a continual push and pull between blood pressure and fluid volume removal. His high oxygen demand remained, but his lungs were less compliant in receiving it. He remained too critically ill for a tracheostomy and a feeding tube. His foot looked worse, and his edema had caused the top of his feet to bubble up in a blister. While I'd been gone, Sue had changed his code status to no CPR. We remained in an uncomfortable holding pattern as the days of the week ticked by.

I touched base with Sue once and had the luck of making the call when Frank was home visiting. The update didn't really provide them with new information. They asked some questions about lung transplant and accepted that it wasn't an option at his age and with multisystem organ damage.

On day forty-one, things changed from critically ill and stable to critically ill and unstable. In Robert's case, it meant worse instead of better. The ICU team reached out to me and asked if I would connect with his family. The rotating teams had been following the palliative medicine notes and knew we had a rapport. Robert was septic again and had reached maximum doses on two pressors with a third being added and titrated up. His oxygen requirements were now 100 percent. Despite maximal levels of support, his body simply couldn't absorb the oxygen or expel the CO2. His blood was becoming acidotic. He was dying.

Cathie and I made the call and reached Sue at home. I was glad to hear background noise to know she wasn't alone. Sue had spoken with Robert's nurse earlier in the morning and had received an update that things were worsening. She was waiting for a call largely to affirm her fears. She sounded worn down.

There were less of the tears and emotions than there had been in earlier weeks. It seemed she had come to understand that he was no longer coming home. I tried to softly use painfully honest clear words.

"I wish I could tell you something different, but it looks like your husband is dying."

Sue asked, "Do you think he can pull through this again?"

The honest answer could come in a variety of forms. I'd seen people rally, but for him, the larger picture was a difficult one, even if everything went right. So, I discussed the larger picture in the shadow of that day.

"I'm worried that his body doesn't have much reserve. We've seen that with his kidneys, his wounds, and his rigid lungs. If he pulls through today, I'm worried we'll have other setbacks before we get to the point of a tracheostomy and that he won't get well enough to leave the ICU. Even if he did somehow make it out of the ICU, I'm less confident that he'll make it far for long. From what you've told me about your husband, I'm concerned about what he would think of a life in a dependent state with dialysis. What we're doing now is no longer prolonging living but prolonging dying."

Sue shared with us that the family had been talking over the weeks and were also worried about what his future would hold. They'd come to an opinion that he was a man who enjoyed work, family, and the open road, and the isolation of a nursing home entrapped by life support was the opposite of what he would want.

Part of the challenge for the Smithington family was their own perceptions of strength. Robert was physically stronger than Sue. She and others in the family had avoided this critically ill picture and were recovering from their experience with COVID. In some ways, their experiences had influenced expectations and their tenacious hope. Sue was now at a different place and revisited some questions we had only touched on in the past.

"How do we stop?"

I told her that we would continue to care for Robert, but the focus of care would be different from critical care support and instead would be on any symptoms of pain or distress while we began to stop things that would prolong the dying process. We'd stop dialysis, stop his pressors, and free his body from the breathing tube. I didn't think he would have much time without those supports given his current level of need. I assured her that with whatever time he had, we would care for him.

"When we begin to switch gears to end of life care, it's one of the times we allow family to visit. Do you or any of your sons want to come?"

Sue wasn't sure what to do. "I don't want to come. It's too much. But Frankie and Gavin do." So, in the closing of the phone call, we agreed that the current supports would continue while his sons had an opportunity to visit. Sue would let them know.

That evening Frank and Gavin came. We had coordinated with the ICU team, and the nursing staff allowed them in. From what I heard the next morning, they stayed for about fifteen minutes and didn't say or ask much. Robert hadn't improved overnight, and his oxygen levels were plunging with things as simple as position changes.

On the morning of day forty-two, I called Sue back to assess where things stood regarding goals of care. She expressed that we should stop critical care supports and "just keep him comfortable."

I asked, "Is anyone else coming to visit or want to be present?"

"No. Nobody else is coming. But could we do a video visit again so people can see him before we let him go?"

I said yes and asked for some time to coordinate with the critical care team. We set a time for 1:00 p.m.

I ended the call and updated the critical care team, nursing, and a few others. Nephrology had been wondering about changes to dialysis, and nursing was trying to decide whether to change out the dialysis filter. I asked nursing for help in setting up an iPad for 1:00 p.m. After that, I stepped away, saw a few more patients in follow-up, and ate lunch. I kept the afternoon as clear as I could to be there for Robert and his family.

I came back before one o'clock and made an agreement with the critical care team. I'd facilitate the bedside goodbye, and they'd place the orders for transitioning to comfort care. Those orders would be carried out at the close of the meeting unless something changed. I began to gear up both mentally and physically.

The physical part was dropping my lab coat over the chair outside the room, donning a yellow gown over my clothes, taking off my surgical mask, and pulling out my reused N95 and putting it on. I crimped the metal nose brace, then put my surgical mask back on over the N95. Next, I put on the goggles. I readjusted the N95 until the fogging stopped and I knew I had a good seal. Then I put on some gloves.

Robert's nurse had been kind enough to dial up the iPad for the video visit. She handed it to me in the anteroom.

At that stage in the pandemic, I'd done more video visits than I can recall. What was different with this connection was that it was more of a conference call video with multiple rooms than two sides—I had five different video households on the call. I made my introductions and acknowledged that I'd spoken to some of the faces before. What followed was a living memorial service.

It was an intimate encounter with Robert's entire family. Sue was there and Paula with her. There were some others with them, including Rex the dog. On a different screen was Frank and his wife, their son who was roughly ten, and a daughter of about fourteen. On a different screen was another son, his spouse, his cousins, and their kids. On a third camera there was Gavin, his spouse, and their toddler and four-year-old. On a fourth camera, another son and his family. On the last camera, the remaining son, his girls, and Rob's brother.

There were far more than I'd anticipated or ever had in a family goodbye meeting before. I realized that we would need to try to have some structure and suggested that each family take a minute in front of the camera to say some things. It seemed that was already their plan, or at least they rolled with the idea readily. With that, I touched the icon to flip the camera away from me and activate the camera on Robert. I pulled up a trash can and sat on the sturdy lid to hold the camera.

In that arrangement, all of the family could see Robert if I held the iPad steady. I could see Robert on the screen if I was doing it correctly and adjust how I held the iPad if the angle or distance was bad. The quirk was that I could see their faces and Robert on the same screen, but they couldn't see me. Sue spoke first in the family, and I became the silent observer, bracing my arm on the bedrail.

On prior visits, Sue had seen her husband and expressed her love and implored him to fight. On this visit, it was statements of love and remembrance and mentions of family who had died. It was permission to go see them. When her voice grew quiet, Paula shifted into view and spoke.

"'Member that time we went fishin' and you slipped in the crick? You drug my ass in with you. Well, I'm gonna miss fishing with you. You go catch some big fish in heaven."

Paula's husband said some words, and then they switched the primary camera to a different household.

There were wood paneled walls and a dark orange chair on a green carpet. I was humbled being invited into their world. One of his granddaughters spoke next and tearfully thanked him for pieces of advice in the past. She shared that it made a difference and told an inside joke that only he would understand. After a minute, she wiped some tears from her face and passed the tablet on her end over to her brother who mumbled, "I love you, Popi," and then wiped the sleeve of his hoody across his nose. He was trying to hold his emotions in and quickly passed off the tablet to his dad.

His dad was one of Robert's sons whom I hadn't spoken with before. He took some time to thank his father for "teaching me everything I know and helping me fly right" and promised to keep taking care of his family and raise them right. He talked a little about the work driving trucks and that he would check in on Mom. He told his father he loved him, and I just sat there invisible, holding the iPad.

The grandkids spoke up again in the background and said, "Bye, Popi."

The camera then switched over to Gavin's household.

I was glad the camera wasn't on me. I felt some expectation, real or not, to keep my composure. I was intermittently switching hands, holding the iPad while using the other to squeeze my mask and test its absorptive capacity. The ventilator and intermittent alarms of Robert's oxygen level dropping created background noise in the room.

Gavin was a tall man with facial features much like his father. He got on camera and thanked his father for all he'd taught him about driving trucks, recalling long haul rides Robert had taken him on as a boy. When his own sons were older, he wanted to do the same for them. His wife spoke up next, tearing up, but he stayed composed next to her. Their four-year-old son was wonderfully oblivious to the emotions and just pounced on his own dad.

Gavin sat back and proceeded to pick up his son, toss him up into the air, and catch him. With each landing, there were the squeals of laughter in the purest form that only little kids can produce. The youngest child was toddling in and out of the room in the background with a dog. It wasn't clear who was following whom. This was unfiltered family in the room despite the distance.

The next son and his family also said their piece in turn.

He asked, "I want to play a song for Dad. It's about trucking. That okay?"

I said, "Yeah, sure."

The music began. I'm neither a truck driver nor a country music fan, and from the perspective of the masked man on the other side of the iPad, it was horrible and perfect.

The song ended as the ventilator alarms and pulse ox alarms began competing for attention. Robert's oxygen numbers were now in the seventies. I quickly switched the camera from Robert to me and informed the family that his oxygen numbers were dropping and we were going to shift the focus to making sure he was comfortable. There was a chorus of "Goodbyes" and "I love yous." Sue thanked us for taking care of him and asked that we give her a call to let her know when her husband passed. I thanked everybody for being a part, and then we closed the connection. Somewhere I lost count, but I think we had twenty-seven different family members on the call.

His ICU nurse and respiratory therapist took over from there and transitioned the focus of care toward comfort. His dialysis and pressor drips were halted. The breathing tube came out shortly after. They continued to clear his airway of secretions as his breathing became erratic. I shed my gear and walked out with a somber feeling of respect for Robert and his family.

Robert died about forty-five minutes later.

Vaccination

In the span of 2020, the work of palliative medicine changed to include a variety of skills for remote consultations as well as more expertise for discussions related to COVID.

The second wave arrived in Pennsylvania between late November of 2020 and January of 2021. In February, I was still seeing numerous patients who got infected over Christmas. Specific factors such as multiple holidays and gatherings could be cited as pushing the surge. Due to Pennsylvania being an electoral battle ground, we also had thirteen super-spreader events in the form of unmasked political rallies that undoubtedly contributed to this surge and latent death toll.

Pfizer's COVID-19 vaccine received FDA authorization on December 11, and the first ICU nurse was vaccinated in New York on December 14.[34] This was awesome news, though it swirled with the uncertainty of when vaccination would reach my practice community, my colleagues, or my family. The problem wasn't the network I practice in. We were no strangers to mass vaccination events due to our annual flu vaccination drive. The concern with the COVID vaccine involved actually getting it to injection centers as well as managing temperature controls.

The vaccine came in fits and starts, with the ICU personnel who were swimming daily in a COVID atmosphere rightly being at the

---

[34] Chas Danner and Matt Stieb, "What We Know About the U.S. COVID-19 Vaccine Distribution Plan," Intelligencer, last modified December 19, 2020, https://nymag.com/intelligencer/2020/12/what-we-know-about-u-s-covid-19-vaccine-distribution-plan.html

front of that line. The messaging for when the palliative medicine team would be called up was unclear. Some of the internal correspondence indicated palliative medicine was considered to fit into a second subset of the first group, them being 1A, and us being 1B. Knowing I'd spent forty-five minutes in a family goodbye video visit at a COVID bedside earlier in the week, I was understandably disheartened by this. I took the time to forward that email to myself for later review at home.

It was a snowy weekend, and as I reread the words, it was apparent that every colleague I'd stood shoulder to shoulder with throughout the past year was in line in front of my team. That hurt. What rubbed salt in the wound was the suggestion that it might be another two months until our group could get vaccinated. I contemplated what to do with this dawning understanding of projected access. I'm not an idle man.

I spent the evening sending correspondence to friends at six different hospitals in four states seeking spare vaccinations, even messaging Pfizer directly to plead my case. I drafted but didn't send an email to the chief of the department of medicine. The larger team was doing the best it could, but in that weekend, I felt so deeply betrayed—I even considered packing up my desk. Resignation hadn't been in the plans, but I couldn't fathom waiting until seemingly everyone else around me was already vaccinated.

The snow meant that I spent the remainder of the weekend sledding with the kids. We met with two of their friends outside on a cool windy hill—it was the closest social gathering we would allow them. I decided to pause and see if my outreach yielded any action, and while I received responses from all of my friends at other hospitals, there was no vaccine.

Monday arrived, and I parked and trudged inside past hundreds of joyous colleagues lined up for their first vaccination. I was thrilled for them, though also quite jealous. During morning rounds, I raised the issue of our place in the vaccination race. I was assured that thousands of vials were arriving weekly. I held that email a bit longer and, at the end of another busy day, walked back out past a line of different smiling faces. Tuesday morning, I walked past that line and noted it wrapped past all of the conference rooms and down the hall past the cafeteria. Things were happening, but all the uncertainty remained.

On Tuesday evening, December 22, I was sitting down at home for a fish dinner with my wife and two girls. There was the normal banter about remote learning, who liked dinner, who didn't, and two dogs begging for a sample. My wife's phone buzzed with a text from Kara, another doctor in her practice. It was 6:55 p.m., and she was letting us know that her sister said there were some unclaimed vaccinations that were thawed and in need of arms. The downside was the vaccination line closed at 7:00, and we lived twelve minutes away. Kara would let us know if she heard more.

We were so close. I got up and changed out of my gym clothes, and the second text came at 7:02. There were a few more vaccinations, but the line was closing at 7:15. I looked up at my wife as I tied my shoes. "We try!" She was in motion in that instant as well. We yelled to the kids that we were going to the hospital, and she called Nana from the road to say the kids were alone for the moment and why we were running.

We drove quickly on hope and prayer. If my car had a flux capacitor, it would've been triggered and left flaming tracks miles from the hospital. We parked and sprinted up the deck stairwell and swiped into the vaccine hall. Were we on time? Where was the check in? Was it true? Was there a catch? We were able to find the check-in station right at 7:15. We gave our work ID numbers and got a sticker.

We were officially in line. Only about six more people made it into the line before vaccination team members announced to those passing by that it was closed.

I still held my breath until we were in the conference room. There was a sense of elation that a shadow was lifting for everyone in that space. Joy! We had joy. We got our shot and took pictures. Danielle and I joked that it was the hottest date we'd been on in the past year—it was the only date, but it was awesome! We sat in the informal observation area for the requisite fifteen minutes.

I was off the next day and texted team members to check for unclaimed vaccinations. All but two received the vaccine the next day. Of those two, one had just recovered from COVID and the other was home with it. Most of us were stepping out of the shadow of death and into the light. Gradually, our families followed.

Conclusion

The COVID-19 pandemic created some unique challenges in how we engage in the work of consultation both in person and remotely, and it's both raging and tapering down as I write these final words. None of us truly know what the future holds. I suspect that this won't be the only pandemic I see in the course of my career, though it's my hope that we have the opportunity to learn from the experience and grow as a society to a better new normal.

The practice of palliative medicine continues to present me with the privilege of connecting with people and their families as they navigate complex illnesses. On most days, I find a sense of joy and connection that results in a feeling of doing fulfilling and meaningful work. Collectively, this joy counterbalances the exposure to those cases that have the deepest sense of loss and suffering, and I find that I've done my best when that human connection is made. All of us have an opportunity to connect as we serve the patients in our care. The time required and allowed to do this in palliative care is one of the greatest assets in my field of practice. This is paired in equal part with the blessing of working alongside an exceptional group of people with diverse skills. I hope this book provided some entertainment as well as insight into the language and role of palliative medicine, whether you work in healthcare or not.

Make the most of each day.

Glossary

ablation: The process of ablating, surgical removal, or chemical and electric destruction of tissue.[35]

Ambu bag: An oxygen reservoir typically attached to a face mask that can be manually compressed to force oxygen into the lungs.

amiodarone drip: An antiarrhythmic drug administered to treat life-threatening ventricular arrhythmias.[36]

anasarca: Generalized edema with accumulation of serum in the connective tissue.[37]

anoscopy: The use of an instrument to facilitate the examination of the anal canal.[38]

anoxic insult: An injury derived from inadequate flow of oxygen to tissue (hypoxia). Often referring to a brain injury following oxygen deprivation sustained during cardiac arrest or respiratory failure.

anticoagulant: A substance that hinders the clotting of blood; blood thinner. Some examples include heparin, coumadin, Plavix, and lovenox.[39]

---

[35] "Ablation," Merriam-Webster (Merriam-Webster), accessed August 20, 2021, https://www.merriam-webster.com/dictionary/ablation#medicalDictionary

[36] "Amiodarone," Merriam-Webster (Merriam-Webster), accessed August 20, 2021, https://www.merriam-webster.com/medical/amiodarone

[37] "Anasarca," Merriam-Webster (Merriam-Webster), accessed August 23, 2021, https://www.merriam-webster.com/dictionary/anasarca

[38] "Anoscope," Merriam-Webster (Merriam-Webster), accessed August 23, 2021, https://www.merriam-webster.com/medical/anoscope

[39] "Anticoagulant," Merriam-Webster (Merriam-Webster), accessed August 23, 2021, https://www.merriam-webster.com/dictionary/anticoagulant

atrial fibrillation: Very rapid uncoordinated contractions of the atria of the heart resulting in a lack of synchronism between heartbeat and pulse beat.[40]

auscultate: To listen, typically with a stethoscope.

bacteremia: The presence of bacteria in the blood. May be without symptoms or progress to sepsis.[41]

BiPAP: Bilevel positive airway pressure.[42] This typically is administered in critical care via a seal-forming face mask capable of delivering pressurized concentrated oxygen during inhalation and with reduced pressure during exhalation.[43]

bronchodilator: A class of drug used to dilate the bronchial passages to allow for gas exchange. Example: Albuterol.

bronchoscopy: A usually flexible endoscope for inspecting or passing instruments into the bronchi of the lungs. This may be performed to observe lung tissue for trauma or pathology, obtain a biopsy, or clear mucous plugs impairing oxygen absorption.[44]

cannula: A small tube.

---

[40] "Atrial Fibrillation," Merriam-Webster (Merriam-Webster), accessed August 23, 2021, https://www.merriam-webster.com/medical/atrial%20fibrillation

[41] "Bacteremia," Merriam-Webster (Merriam-Webster), accessed August 23, 2021, https://www.merriam-webster.com/dictionary/bacteremia

[42] "Bipap," Merriam-Webster (Merriam-Webster), accessed August 20, 2021, https://www.merriam-webster.com/dictionary/BiPAP

[43] "Bilevel Positive Airway Pressure," Merriam-Webster (Merriam-Webster), accessed August 20, 2021, https://www.merriam-webster.com/dictionary/bilevel%20positive%20airway%20pressure

[44] "Bronchoscopy," Merriam-Webster (Merriam-Webster), accessed August 23, 2021, https://www.merriam-webster.com/dictionary/bronchoscopy

carcinomatosis: The diffuse spread of cancer beyond its primary source. Commonly occurring in the abdominal space.

cerebral edema: The accumulation of fluid in and resultant swelling of the brain that may be caused by trauma, a tumor, lack of oxygen at high altitudes, or exposure to toxic substances.[45]

cisatracurium (brand Nimbex): A skeletal muscle relaxant that blocks neuromuscular transmission. This drug is also known as a paralytic and has use during endotracheal intubation. In profound respiratory failure, paralysis also reduces oxygen demand.[46]

cold caloric test: The slow instillation of cold water into the ear canal causing hyperpolarization of the hair cells and inhibition of the vestibular nerve, resulting in a fast component of the nystagmus beating away from the stimulating ear. This test may be used to examine brain stem integrity.[47]

dysplasia: Abnormal tissue growth. Significant as a pre-cancerous risk.

dyspnea: Difficulty breathing or shortness of breath.

electrophysiology: Physiology that is concerned with the electrical aspects of physiological phenomena.[48] In the book, this

---

[45] "Cerebral Edema," Merriam-Webster (Merriam-Webster), accessed August 23, 2021, https://www.merriam-webster.com/medical/cerebral%20edema

[46] "Cisatracurium," Uses, Interactions, Mechanism of Action, DrugBank Online, last modified August 19, 2021, https://go.drugbank.com/drugs/DB00565

[47] Sunil Munakomi, "Caloric Reflex Test," StatPearls [Internet], U.S. National Library of Medicine, last modified February 27, 2021, https://www.ncbi.nlm.nih.gov/books/NBK557481/

[48] "Electrophysiology," Merriam-Webster (Merriam-Webster), accessed August 20, 2021, https://www.merriam-webster.com/dictionary/electrophysiology

refers to the electrical conduction within the heart to coordinate a rhythm.

encephalopathy: A disease of the brain.[49] An encephalopathic state may be the result of trauma, medications, infection, or a toxic metabolic state. In some cases, this is a reversible or modifiable state following treatment or resolution of underlying causes.

endotracheal tube: A small, usually plastic tube inserted into the trachea through the mouth or nose to maintain an unobstructed passageway, especially to deliver oxygen or anesthesia to the lungs. Typically connected to a ventilator or transiently an Ambu bag.[50]

hemoptysis: Coughing up of blood from the lungs.[51]

hepatorenal failure: Cascading organ failure originating with the liver. In cirrhosis, or liver cancer, combined with profound protein deficiency, blood flow may meet resistance at the liver and be shunted to soft tissue. This in turn deprives other organs of adequate fluid volume resulting in injury.

herniation: To protrude through an abnormal body opening.[52]

high resolution anoscopy: The visualization of the anal canal under magnification, often with the use of iodine-based contrast solutions for the purpose of identifying and treating pre-cancerous lesions.

---

[49] "Encephalopathic," Merriam-Webster (Merriam-Webster), accessed August 20, 2021, https://www.merriam-webster.com/dictionary/encephalopathic

[50] "Endotracheal Tube," Merriam-Webster (Merriam-Webster), accessed August 20, 2021, https://www.merriam-webster.com/dictionary/endotracheal%20tube

[51] "Hemoptysis," Merriam-Webster (Merriam-Webster), accessed August 20, 2021, https://www.merriam-webster.com/dictionary/hemoptysis

[52] "Herniation," Merriam-Webster (Merriam-Webster), accessed August 20, 2021, https://www.merriam-webster.com/dictionary/herniation

human lymphocyte antigen (HLA): A type of molecule found on the surface of most cells in the body. Human lymphocyte antigens play an important part in the body's immune response to foreign substances. They make up a person's tissue type, which varies from person to person. Human lymphocyte antigen tests are done before a donor stem cell or organ transplant to find out if tissues match between the donor and the person receiving the transplant. Also called HLA and human leukocyte antigen.[53]

hydroxychloroquine: A drug derived from quinolone that is taken orally in the form of its sulfate to treat malaria, rheumatoid arthritis, and lupus erythematosus.[54]

hypercoagulable state: A state or condition marked by an increased tendency to form blood clots within a blood vessel: excessive coagulability.[55]

ischemia: Deficient supply of blood to a body part, such as the heart or brain, that is due to obstruction of the inflow of arterial blood.[56]

ischemic stroke: A lack of oxygen to a territory of the brain from blockage of blood flow, typical embolic in nature. This is

---

[53] "NCI Dictionary of Cancer TERMS," National Cancer Institute, accessed August 23, 2021, https://www.cancer.gov/publications/dictionaries/cancer-terms/def/human-lymphocyte-antigen

[54] "Hydroxychloroquine," Merriam-Webster (Merriam-Webster), accessed August 23, 2021, https://www.merriam-webster.com/dictionary/hydroxychloroquine

[55] "Hypercoagulable," Merriam-Webster (Merriam-Webster), accessed August 23, 2021, https://www.merriam-webster.com/dictionary/hypercoagulable

[56] "Ischemia," Merriam-Webster (Merriam-Webster), accessed August 20, 2021, https://www.merriam-webster.com/dictionary/ischemia

differentiated from hemorrhagic stroke with results in a lack of oxygenation from rupture of a blood vessel within the brain.

kyphosis: Exaggerated outward curvature of the thoracic region of the spine resulting in a rounded upper back.[57] Note, this curvature may impede full expansion of the lung, impairing breathing or tolerance of pulmonary illness.

MCA territory: Middle cerebral artery, the most significant arterial circulation within the brain. Strokes are often described by which component of MCA circulation is affected.

metoprolol: A beta-blocker used to treat high blood pressure and angina.[58]

mural thrombus: A blood clot (thrombus) forming in the wall of a blood vessel.

myocardial infarction (MI): Death of heart muscle from lack of oxygen commonly known as a heart attack.

Optiflow™: High-flow nasal cannula capable of giving concentrated oxygen at rates of sixty liters per minute.

Oxygen saturation: Refers to the percentage of hemoglobin molecules carrying oxygen in circulation. This is normally 95 percent unaided.

pancytopenia: An abnormal reduction in the number of erythrocytes, white blood cells, and blood platelets in the blood.[59]

paroxysmal AFib: see atrial fibrillation. Paroxysmal describes atrial fibrillation in its rapid or uncontrolled state.

partial glossectomy: The surgical removal of part of the tongue.

partial lobectomy: The surgical removal of a portion of the lung.

---

[57] "Kyphosis," Merriam-Webster (Merriam-Webster), accessed August 20, 2021, https://www.merriam-webster.com/dictionary/kyphosis

[58] "Metoprolol," Merriam-Webster (Merriam-Webster), accessed August 20, 2021, https://www.merriam-webster.com/dictionary/metoprolol

[59] "Pancytopenia," Merriam-Webster (Merriam-Webster), accessed August 23, 2021, https://www.merriam-webster.com/dictionary/pancytopenia

PEG tube: Percutaneous endoscopic gastrostomy tube. A feeding tube placed through the abdominal wall for long-term feeding.

PleurX™ Drain: A drainage system designed to drain abnormal fluid collections. Most commonly, these include pleural effusions (around the lung), ascites (abdominal), or malignant (arising from cancer).[60]

pneumothorax: A condition in which air or other gas is present in the pleural cavity (space around the lung) and which occurs spontaneously as a result of disease or injury of lung tissue, rupture of air-filled pulmonary cysts, or puncture of the chest wall or is induced as a therapeutic measure to collapse the lung.[61]

pressor: A class of drug used to raise blood pressure in the critical care setting. Used in the treatment of shock and acting by increasing vascular tone.

Propofol: A fast-acting intravenous sedative with a short half-life used for general anesthesia or sedation during periods of ventilator support. Trade name is Diprovan.

thoracentesis: Aspiration of fluid from the chest as in empyema or pleural effusion.[62]

thoracoabdominal aneurysm: Bulging and weakness in the wall of the aorta that extends from the chest into the abdomen. The

---

[60] "Patient Information – Pleurx™ System," BD, accessed August 23, 2021, https://www.bd.com/en-us/offerings/capabilities/drainage/peritoneal-and-pleural-drainage/about-the-pleurx-drainage-system/patient-information-pleurx-system

[61] "Pneumothorax," Merriam-Webster (Merriam-Webster), accessed August 20, 2021, https://www.merriam-webster.com/dictionary/pneumothorax

[62] "Thoracentesis," Merriam-Webster (Merriam-Webster), accessed August 20, 2021, https://www.merriam-webster.com/medical/thoracentesis

aorta is the largest blood vessel in the body, and it delivers blood from the heart to the rest of the body.[63]

thrombectomy: Surgical removal of a blood clot.[64]

troponin spike: Troponin as a protein marker released from cardiac cells when damaged. A spike in troponin is indicative of damage.

---

[63] "Thoracoabdominal Aortic Aneurysm," Thoracoabdominal Aortic Aneurysm UVA Health (UVA Health), accessed August 20, 2021, https://uvahealth.com/services/aneurysm-treatment/thoracoabdominal-aortic-aneurysm

[64] "Thrombectomy," Merriam-Webster (Merriam-Webster), accessed August 20, 2021, https://www.merriam-webster.com/medical/thrombectomy

Author Bio

Craig C. Durie was born in North Carolina and raised in Bethlehem, Pennsylvania, after his parents emigrated from South Africa.

He now lives in Allentown, Pennsylvania, with his wife and two daughters.

He has twenty-five years' experience in healthcare with work in Maryland, Delaware, Pennsylvania, and New York.

Craig is a certified registered nurse practitioner (CRNP) who holds a doctorate in nursing practice (DNP), a certification as an Advanced Certified Hospice and Palliative Nurse (ACHPN), and a certification as a Registered Nurse First Assist (RNFA).

When he's not working, Craig enjoys gardening, traveling, kayaking, mountain biking, and hiking, and he even spent a brief period as a hang-glider pilot. When he needs an escape, he enjoys drinking coffee while reading a good sci-fi book.

Bibliography

"Ablation." Merriam-Webster. Merriam-Webster. Accessed August 20, 2021. https://www.merriam-webster.com/dictionary/ablation# medical Dictionary

All That's Interesting. "When 'Blowing Smoke Up Your Ass' Was Much More Than Just A Saying." All That's Interesting. Last modified March 6, 2020. https://allthatsinteresting.com/blowing-smoke-up-your-ass

"Amiodarone." Merriam-Webster. Merriam-Webster. Accessed August 20, 2021. https://www.merriam-webster.com/medical/amiodarone

"Anasarca." Merriam-Webster. Merriam-Webster. Accessed August 23, 2021. https://www.merriam-webster.com/dictionary/anasarca

"Anoscope." Merriam-Webster. Merriam-Webster. Accessed August 23, 2021. https://www.merriam-webster.com/medical/anoscope

"Anticoagulant." Merriam-Webster. Merriam-Webster. Accessed August 23, 2021. https://www.merriam-webster.com/dictionary/anticoagulant

"Atrial Fibrillation." Merriam-Webster. Merriam-Webster. Accessed August 23, 2021. https://www.merriam-webster.com/medical/atrial%20fibrillation

"Bacteremia." Merriam-Webster. Merriam-Webster. Accessed August 23, 2021. https://www.merriam-webster.com/dictionary/bacteremia

"Bilevel Positive Airway Pressure." Merriam-Webster. Merriam-Webster. Accessed August 20, 2021. https://www.merriam-webster.com/dictionary/bilevel%20positive%20airway%20pressure

"Bipap." Merriam-Webster. Merriam-Webster. Accessed August 20, 2021. https://www.merriam-webster.com/dictionary/BiPAP

Boyle, D. K., P. A. Miller, and S. A. Forbes-Thompson. "Communication and end-of-life care in the intensive care unit." *Critical Care Nursing Quarterly* 11, no. 4 (2005): 302–316

"Bronchoscopy." Merriam-Webster. Merriam-Webster. Accessed August 23, 2021. https://www.merriam-webster.com/dictionary/bronchoscopy

"Cerebral Edema." Merriam-Webster. Merriam-Webster. Accessed August 23, 2021. https://www.merriam-webster.com/medical/cerebral%20edema

"Cisatracurium." Uses, Interactions, Mechanism of Action | DrugBank Online. Last modified August 19, 2021.
https://go.drugbank.com/drugs/DB00565

Danner, Chas, and Matt Stieb. "What We Know About the U.S. COVID-19 Vaccine Distribution Plan." Intelligencer. Last modified December 19, 2020. https://nymag.com/intelligencer/2020/12/what-we-know-about-u-s-covid-19-vaccine-distribution-plan.html

DiMasi, J., H. Grabowski, and R. Hansen. "Innovation in the pharmaceutical industry: New estimates of R&D costs." *Journal of Health Economics* 47 (2016): 20–33. doi.org/10.1016/j.jhealeco. 2016.01.012

Del Gaudio, F., T. I. Zaider, M. Brier, and D. W. Kissane. "Challenges in providing family-centered support to families in palliative care." *Palliative Medicine* 26, no. 8 (2011): 1025–1033. doi:10.1177/ 0269216311426919

Center for Advancing Palliative Care. "About Palliative Care: What Is Palliative Care?" Last modified September 7, 2016. https://www.capc .org/about/palliative-care/

"Electrophysiology." Merriam-Webster. Merriam-Webster. Accessed August 20, 2021. https://www.merriam-webster.com/dictionary/electrophysiology

"Encephalopathic." Merriam-Webster. Merriam-Webster. Accessed August 20, 2021. https://www.merriam-webster.com/dictionary/encephalopathic

"Endotracheal Tube." Merriam-Webster. Merriam-Webster. Accessed August 20, 2021. https://www.merriam-webster.com/dictionary/ endotracheal%20tube

Enguidanos, S., P. Housen, M. Penido, B. Mejia, and J. A. Miller. "Family members perceptions of inpatient palliative care consult services: A qualitative study." *Palliative Medicine* 28, no. 1 (2014): 42–48. doi:10.1177/0269216313491620

"Hemoptysis." Merriam-Webster. Merriam-Webster. Accessed August 20, 2021. https://www.merriam-webster.com/dictionary/hemoptysis

"Herniation." Merriam-Webster. Merriam-Webster. Accessed August 20, 2021. https://www.merriam-webster.com/dictionary/herniation

Hudson, P., T. Thomas, and K. Quinn. "Family meetings in palliative care: Are they effective?" *Palliative Medicine* 23 (2009): 150–157. doi:10.1177/0269216308099960

"Hydroxychloroquine." Merriam-Webster. Merriam-Webster. Accessed August 23, 2021. https://www.merriam-webster.com/dictionary/hydroxychloroquine

"Hypercoagulable." Merriam-Webster. Merriam-Webster. Accessed August 23, 2021. https://www.merriam-webster.com/dictionary/hypercoagulable

"Ischemia." Merriam-Webster. Merriam-Webster. Accessed August 20, 2021. https://www.merriam-webster.com/dictionary/ischemia

Kouwenhoven, W. B., J. R. Jude, and G. G. Knickerbocker. "CLOSED-CHEST CARDIAC MASSAGE." *JAMA* 173, no. 10 (1960):1064–1067. doi:10.1001/jama.1960.03020280004002

Krochmal, R., W. Blenko, M. Afshar, G. Netzer, S .Roy, D. Weigand, and C. Shanholtz. "Family presence at first cardiopulmonary resucitation and subsequent limitations on care in the medical intensive care unit." *American Association of Critical Care Nurses* 26, no. 3 (2017): 221–228. doi: 10.4037/ajcc2017510

"Kyphosis." Merriam-Webster. Merriam-Webster. Accessed August 20, 2021. https://www.merriam-webster.com/dictionary/kyphosis

May, P., M. M. Garrido, B. Cassel, A. S. Kelley, D. E. Meier, C. Normand, and S. R. Morrison. "Prospective cohort study of hospital palliative care teams for inpatients with advanced cancer: Earlier consultation is associated with larger cost-saving effect." *Journal of Clinical Oncology* 33 (2015): 2745–2752. doi:10.1200/JCO.2014.60.2334

"Metoprolol." Merriam-Webster. Merriam-Webster. Accessed August 20, 2021. https://www.merriam-webster.com/dictionary/metoprolol

Morrison, S. R., J. Dietrich, S. Ladwig, T. Quill, J. Sacco, J. Tangeman, and D. E. Meier. "Palliative care consultation teams cut hospital costs for medicaid beneficiaries." *Health Affairs* 30 (2011): 454–463. doi:10.1377/hlthaff.2010.0929

Morrison, S. R., J. D. Penrod, B. J. Cassel, M. Caust-Ellenbogen, A. Litke, L. Spragens, and D. E. Meir. "Cost savings associated with U.S. hospital palliative care consultation programs." *Archives of Internal Medicine* 168 (2008): 1783–1790

Mueller, C., L. M. Lord, M. Marian, S. McClave, and S. J. Miller. (2017). *The ASPEN adult nutrition support core curriculum* 39, no. 3: Ethics and Law

Munakomi, Sunil. "Caloric Reflex Test." StatPearls [Internet]. U.S. National Library of Medicine, February 27, 2021. https://www.ncbi. nlm.nih.gov/books/NBK557481/

"NCI Dictionary of Cancer TERMS." National Cancer Institute. Accessed August 23, 2021. https://www.cancer.gov/publications/dictionaries/cancer-terms/def/human-lymphocyte-antigen

Norton, S. A., L. A. Hogan, R. G. Holloway, H. Temkin-Greener, M. J. Buckley, and T. E. Quill. "Proactive palliative care in the medcal intensive care unit: Effects of length of stay for selected high-risk patients." *Critical Care Medicine* 35 (2007): 1530–1535. doi:10.1097/01.CCM.0000266533.06543.OC

"Pancytopenia." Merriam-Webster. Merriam-Webster. Accessed August 23, 2021. https://www.merriam-webster.com/dictionary/pancytopenia

"Patient Information – Pleurx™ System." BD. Accessed August 23, 2021. https://www.bd.com/en-us/offerings/capabilities/drainage/peritoneal-and-pleural-drainage/about-the-pleurx-drainage-system/patient-information-pleurx-system

"Pneumothorax." Merriam-Webster. Merriam-Webster. Accessed August 20, 2021. https://www.merriam-webster.com/dictionary/pneumothorax

Shaw, Elizabeth. "The History of CPR." ProCPR. Last modified April 10, 2019. https://www.procpr.org/blog/misc/history-of-cpr

Sullivan, S. S., C. Ferreira da rosa Silva, and M. A. Meeker. "Family meetings at end of life: A systematic review." *Journal of Hospice and Palliative Nursing* 17, no.3 (2015): 196–205. doi:10.107/NJH.0000000000000147

Swank, K., K. McCartan, R. Kapoor, N. Gada, I. Diak, Department of Health and Human Services Public Health Service Food and Drug Administration Center for Drug Evaluation and Research Office of Surveillance and Epidemiology Pharmacovigilance

Memorandum. Accessed May 19, 2020. https://www.accessdata.fda.gov/drugsatfda_docs/nda/2020/OSE%20Review_Hydroxychloroquine-Cholorquine%20-%2019May2020_Redacted.pdf

Temel, J. S., J. A. Greer, A. Muzikansky, E. R. Gallagher, S. Admane, V. A. Jackson, and T. J. Lynch. "Early palliative care for patients with metastatic non-small cell lung cancer." *The New England Journal of Medicine* 363 (2010): 733–742. doi: 10.1056/NEJMoa1000678

"Thoracentesis." Merriam-Webster. Merriam-Webster. Accessed August 20, 2021. https://www.merriam-webster.com/medical/thoracentesis

"Thoracoabdominal Aortic Aneurysm." Thoracoabdominal Aortic Aneurysm | UVA Health. UVA Health. Accessed August 20, 2021. https://uvahealth.com/services/aneurysm-treatment/thoracoabdominal-aortic-aneurysm

"Thrombectomy." Merriam-Webster. Merriam-Webster. Accessed August 20, 2021. https://www.merriam-webster.com/medical/thrombectomy

"Transplant Medicine: MELD Score and 90-Day Mortality Rate for Alcoholic Hepatitis." Mayo Clinic. Mayo Foundation for Medical Education and Research. Accessed June 5, 2021. https://www.mayoclinic.org/medical-professionals/transplant-medicine/calculators/meld-score-and-90-day-mortality-rate-for-alcoholic-hepatitis/itt-20434719

Zimmerman, Jack E. MD, FCCM; Andrew A. Kramer, PhD; Douglas S. McNair, MD, PhD; Fern M. Malila, RN, MS; Violet L. Shaffer, MA. "Intensive care unit length of stay: Benchmarking based on Acute Physiology and Chronic Health Evaluation (APACHE) IV." *Critical Care Medicine* 34, no. 10 (October 2006): 2517–2529. doi: 10.1097/01.CCM.0000240233.01711.D9

Made in the USA
Middletown, DE
16 January 2022